The Thread of Life

JOHN C. KENDREW
F.R.S. Nobel Laureate

The Thread of Life
an introduction to molecular biology

based on the series
of B.B.C. Television Lectures
of the same title

HARVARD UNIVERSITY PRESS
CAMBRIDGE MASSACHUSETTS
1968

First published 1966
Reprinted 1967, 1968

Printed in Great Britain

Preface

THIS book is based on a series of television lectures on molecular biology which I delivered early in 1964. I was pleased when the B.B.C. asked me to give the lectures, because it seemed to me that molecular biology was a subject perfectly suited to a non-specialist audience. Anyone should be able to understand it easily without being trained as a scientist; we all find it natural to be interested in biology because we ourselves, being living organisms, are part of its subject matter; and, finally, molecular biology is advancing with such tremendous rapidity that it should be possible to communicate some of the excitement which scientists feel when a whole area of knowledge is quickly being illuminated by new understanding and by a new synthesis of hitherto unconnected facts. I had the same considerations in mind when I was writing the book, and I hope it will help those who are not themselves scientists to share some of the interest and excitement of this new approach to the study of living things.

I am deeply grateful to Mr. Alan Sleath of the B.B.C., who produced the television programme with infinite understanding and tolerance of the problems facing a novice, and to Miss Fiona Holmes and Mr. Bill Haddow who assisted him and greatly helped me as well. I am grateful also to many colleagues who lent me models and pictures, and to Mr. Keith Roberts who made some of the drawings. Finally, I owe more than I could easily convey to my secretary Miss Christabel Raker, who typed several versions of the manuscript and helped me in all sorts of other ways.

Cambridge   J. C. K.
February 1966

5

Contents

Contents

The Plates

38. Greatly enlarged picture of polysomes. Ribosomes are strung along a dark thread, which is a single molecule of messenger RNA

39. Electron microscope picture of a typical 'spherical' virus

40. *a* and *b*. A bacteriophage before becoming attached to its host cell. *a*. Model. *b*. Electron microscope photograph.

    c and *d*. A bacteriophage after becoming attached to its host cell. *c*. Model. *d*. Electron microscope photograph

41. Bacteriophage which has burst open so that its nucleic acid has emerged as an immensely long single molecule

42. A group of bacteriophages

43. Bacteriophages attached to a bacterial membrane

44. Electron microscope picture of particles of tobacco mosaic virus

45. X-ray photograph of tobacco mosaic virus

46. Model of part of a tobacco mosaic virus particle

47. Double-shadowed particles of *Tipula* Iridescent virus

48. Double-shadowed particle of *Tipula* Iridescent virus and, for comparison, a double-shadowed model of an icosahedron

49. Single particle of adenovirus, showing triangular faces

50. A model adenovirus constructed from 252 ping-pong balls

51. A particle of Orf virus, with a drawing of a model for comparison

52. A photomicrograph of a single chromosome showing the band pattern and puffs where a section of the chromosome is actively engaged in producing messenger RNA

Tyger! Tyger! burning bright
In the forests of the night,
What immortal hand or eye,
Dare frame thy fearful symmetry?

WILLIAM BLAKE

I

The Revolution in Biology

DURING the last fifteen years or so there has been something of a revolution in biology. It is a revolution that has been associated with the name 'molecular biology', and in this book my object is to explain simply how this revolution came about and some of the exciting results it has achieved, and to try to give an idea of the new picture we have of the way living organisms work as a result of the research of the last few years.

Revolutions are often characterized by the appearance of outsiders. This one in biology is no exception. Indeed, to a large extent it has been carried out by people who were trained not as biologists, but as physicists, chemists, or mathematicians even. As we shall see, there is nothing accidental about this.

My own history is a typical example. I was trained as a chemist, and my interests were especially in organic chemistry, which is the branch of the subject dealing with the compounds of carbon. Traditionally, chemists studied the carbon compounds in the test tube and without much reference to the living organisms of which they are typical—because, of course, carbon compounds are really the essential components of all living things, and indeed form almost the total solid substance of every plant and animal.

I remember, when I was a schoolboy in the middle 'thirties, seeing in one of my text-books the X-ray picture of a human hair, reproduced in Plate 1. Such a picture is obtained by taking a powerful beam of X-rays from an X-ray tube, putting the hair into the beam and setting up a photographic plate behind it. You allow the plate to be exposed, for several hours perhaps. At the end of that time when you develop the plate you find this strange and rather messy pattern on it. What does such a pattern mean? It has been known for quite a number of years that if you take X-ray pictures of this kind (they are called X-ray diffraction pictures) of substances in which the molecules are *ordered*, that is in which they are in regular array, like soldiers on parade, then on the plate you get a series of more or less sharp reflections, or blackenings, where beams of X-rays have been bounced off the regular arrays of molecules. If on the other hand the molecules are disordered, irregularly arranged, then no sharp reflections are observed. It is rather like the difference between a football crowd and soldiers on parade. In the football crowd people are all higgledy-piggledy, and if you have molecules heaped together like that you do not get sharp reflections because the X-rays are bounced off each molecule in a different direction, but if there are regular rows of molecules like the soldiers then you do get such reflections—the X-rays are bounced off each row of atoms in the same direction, and add up to give a visible spot. So the fact that we get a pattern of this kind from a human hair shows that the molecules in the hair must be *ordered*.

X-ray patterns like this were first photographed by Professor W. T. Astbury back in the twenties. Incidentally, Astbury, besides being interested in proteins, was passionately fond of music, and years later when he was lent a lock of Mozart's hair, he took an X-ray photograph of it and found precisely the same molecular pattern (Plate 2). He once told me that photographing Mozart's hair, and finding that it revealed exactly the same X-ray pattern as a common mortal's hair, was one of the most exciting things he had ever done. But it was not until about thirty years after he took the first photograph that it was possible to explain what the pattern actually *meant*, in molecular terms. Figure 1 shows the model of the molecules in the hair which it was possible to build once the pattern had been explained, and we shall return later to discuss what this particular arrangement of atoms means and why it is important.

Quite apart from the meaning of this particular ordered arrangement of atoms in the molecules of the hair, the very existence of order of this kind seemed to me very surprising

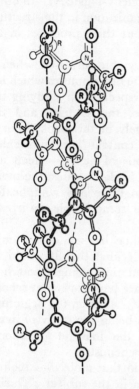

Fig. 1. Model of the α-helix. The main chain is arranged in a right-handed helix and extends indefinitely above and below the picture; successive turns of the helix are held together by weak hydrogen bonds (dotted lines). The side chains are not shown in the picture, but would be attached at the points marked R. This is the arrangement of the polypeptide chain in hair and in many other proteins, and it was discovered by L. Pauling, R. B. Corey and H. R. Branson in 1950.

Low, B. W., & Edsall, J. T. (1956) in Currents in Biochemical Research, *ed.* D. E. Green, p. 378. New York: Interscience.

when I first saw the picture. We are used to the idea of ordered molecules in the inorganic world, in crystals, in rocks, in minerals, but we think of living organisms as easily deformable—flexible, soft, squashy. It is at first sight surprising, when something is as soft as this, that inside it somewhere there could be these regular arrays of molecules like the soldiers on parade.

But perhaps, on reflection, it is not so surprising after all that the molecules of living organisms must be ordered. Any living thing can be likened to a giant factory, a factory producing chemicals, producing energy and motion, indeed reproducing itself too (which most factories cannot do!), and if one thinks of the way in which assembly lines are organized in factories one realizes immediately that all this complex of operations could not be carried out unless they were in some way organized, separated into compartments, not higgledy-piggledy. In other words there must be some kind of organization in the structure of an animal to enable it to carry out these processes in an orderly way.

However that may be, I certainly felt surprised when I saw the picture, and this was one of the first impulses which led me to be interested in biology, and especially in studying the large molecules in living organisms, the proteins and the nucleic acids which will feature largely in this book. For it is these large molecules—and in this context 'large molecules' mean molecules containing thousands of atoms—which are characteristic of living things, and it is also because the molecules composing living things are so large and complicated that studying them is, at any rate for some people, an irresistible challenge.

So it happened that I and many others like me, even though we were not trained as biologists, decided that it would be tremendously fascinating to spend our time doing research in biology using the tools of the trades we had learned at school, the methods of physics and chemistry. Thus in the beginning molecular biology was thought of as being the study of living organisms by scientists using, not the tools of traditional biology, but the tools of physics and chemistry.

Before going further it must be said that molecular biology was by no means the first revolution in the subject. During the emergence of biology as a scientific discipline there has indeed been a whole succession of revolutions.

One might start with Linnaeus. It occurred to me, as I sat in an Alpine meadow on holiday last summer and looked round at the vast diversity of living things around me, insects, animals, plants, all different shapes and sizes and in an incredible variety, what a challenge it must have been to try to reduce this multifariousness of life to some kind of order. And that indeed is just what Linnaeus did when he introduced the classification of animals and plants which bears his name and which is used to this day. In its time Linnaeus' classification was indeed a revolution because it set the stage for the systematic study of living organisms.

The existence of a classification naturally led to the question of the relationship between different kinds of plant and animal, and to the notion of one species emerging from another—in other words, to the concept of *evolution*. The formulation of this concept, and the understanding of the forces of natural selection responsible for evolutionary changes, was a second revolution—and this, of course, was the revolution particularly associated with the name of Darwin. At about the same time yet another revolution took place, the emergence of the 'cell theory'. If you look at any living organism through a microscope you will find that it is made up of a large number of cells (Plate 3). The cell is in a sense the atom of biology. Just as different chemicals are made up of *atoms*, and we know from the work of the physicists that all atoms have a strong family resemblance one to another, with the massive positively-charged nucleus and its surrounding clouds of circulating electrons like a miniature solar system, so in biology we find that every living thing is made up of a large conglomerate of *cells* that have a strong family resemblance to one another. Each has a dense region in the middle, called the *nucleus*, which swims in the *cytoplasm*, a kind of semi-liquid region around it. The whole is enclosed in the *cell membrane* (see Plate 4).

A most important sequel to the discovery of cells, enormously simplifying the task of biologists, was the finding that cells of different types resemble one another rather closely; there are strong family likenesses between the cells of different parts of the same organism, and between the cells of different types of organisms, plants and animals for example. So it makes sense to think about a generalized cell independently of the organism from which it is derived, and this gives us a valuable general approach to the whole living kingdom.

We can, for example, develop the concept of the individual cell as a chemical factory; and this is where yet another revolution took its start, the revolution of biochemistry. To take a very simple example which has been known about for

B

thousands of years, a yeast cell produces alcohol, and of course all alcoholic drinks derive from the action of yeast on various sugary substances. But from the point of view of the yeast cell, the alcohol is simply a by-product. What the yeast cell wants is energy—energy to live. One of the first biological chemical processes which was disentangled by biochemists was the sequence of operations by which living cells, not only yeast, but many others too, produce energy from sugar. Figure 2 gives a picture of the cycle of operations. You can see that it is very complicated. Here we have long sequences of chemical reactions, each leading into the next, in the course of which sugar is broken down into smaller molecules which may be alcohol or may be others, and energy is produced.

I do not want to explain this picture at all. I have included it simply to demonstrate how complicated the cycle of operations is. I want you to remember that it is only one among hundreds of other similar, and just as complicated, activities carried out by every living cell within a volume more than a million million times smaller than that occupied by a complete human being.

The biochemists started off using the traditional techniques of chemistry. These are techniques which can readily handle small molecules, containing say twenty or thirty atoms. The limitations of this approach derived from the fact that most of the really important molecules in living organisms are very much larger than this. They contain thousands of atoms in each molecule instead of tens. At this point the traditional chemical techniques, though developed to a very high point of sophistication, in effect reached their limit. It was here that molecular biology, with its new techniques for studying very large molecules, began to make a significant impact on the subject. It is the nature of this impact which I want to describe here.

Right at the outset I must stress the importance of new techniques. If you consider the series of revolutions I have been describing you will see that in a sense we have been going from the large to the small. We start by studying the whole organism, we go down to the cell and then to the individual molecules of which it is composed. So we have to develop

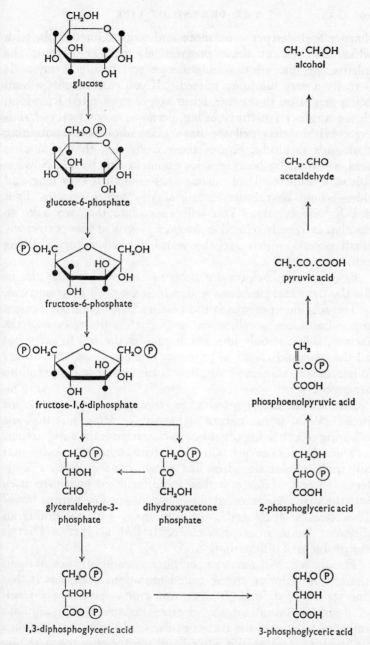

Fig. 2. The fermentation of sugar (glucose) to alcohol. Twelve chemical reactions take place in sequence, each being regulated by a different enzyme.

sharper and sharper eyes, more and more refined tools, with
which to look at these progressively smaller objects; the
microscope, the electron microscope and finally X-rays. It
is really a very big jump indeed. If you can imagine a man
being magnified to the size, let us say, of the United Kingdom,
then a single cell might be as big, perhaps, as one factory building. Within that cell we have giant molecules containing
thousands of atoms: one of these molecules, that of nucleic
acid, we shall be hearing a lot about in this book. Now on
this scale a molecule of nucleic acid—which is very long and
thin—would be thinner than a single piece of electric light
flex in our factory. You will appreciate that we have to
develop extremely refined techniques to look at these extremely
small objects which are the working parts of every living
cell.

Before we embark on our survey of the new biology, let us
list the principal problems with which we shall be concerned.

The first one perhaps is the best understood at the present
time—how does a cell work, and what is the nature of the
factory, this assembly line which enables the cell to carry out
all the manifold chemical processes it needs to be alive at all?
What are the machine tools, how is the sequence of operations
arranged?

The second major problem is—how does a cell reproduce
itself? What is the nature of heredity? How is it that the
offspring of any living organism so closely resembles its parents?

Then there is the question of differentiation. We know that
any multicellular organism, like a man, develops from a single
fertilized egg. How is it this single fertilized egg turns itself
into the vastly complicated object which we call a human baby?
How does a single cell grow into many cells, of numerous
different kinds, in a precisely controlled manner? That is
the problem of differentiation.

Finally we shall mention the phenomenon of discontinuous
changes in animals, the so-called mutations. How is it that
one species of animal changes into a new species as a result
of desirable mutations, by degrees improving the animal's
capacity to exist in the corner of the world where it has taken
its abode? And on the other hand we are only too painfully

aware that there are also *undesirable* mutations leading to disease and deformity. Can we understand these too?

Those are some of the problems we have to address ourselves to.

It is a different situation perhaps from the situation in physics. Some readers may have studied the theory of relativity, for example. I have to warn them that our present subject is a very different one. Instead of explaining rather simple observations by a very sophisticated and subtle intellectual analysis, as the physicist does, we have in biology to deal with a very large and complicated range simply of brute facts: facts about what an organism is like, what reactions it carries out, what sort of cells it is composed of. And what we want to do is to link together these brute facts into a simple unified scheme. The concepts we shall need are rather simple by comparison with those of relativity, even if the facts we are trying to explain are more complicated.

One might ask whether there are any limits to this approach. It is often said that scientists do not believe in miracles. And it is asked how the scientific approach can possibly 'explain' living organisms, especially man, who is the crowning miracle of the universe.

I think this formulation rather misses the point, for in fact biologists approach the challenge of complicated phenomena simply by saying, 'Let us see if we can discover how this animal works. Never mind how far we can go along the road of explanation, it is simply interesting to go along with it as far as we can, using whatever tools we can devise.' We do not even know if there *are* any limits. Certainly in the field of biology they are not yet visible. We have already learned a great deal, and what we have learned is the subject of later chapters in this book.

Whether eventually there are limits beyond which one cannot go is a matter which the biologist, *qua* biologist, really does not care about, simply because he has far too many interesting things to do, right now, without worrying too much if he is going to come up against a dead stop later on.

In this first chapter we have taken a preliminary look at some of the questions about living organisms which biologists have tried to answer in the past, and at the questions we are interested in today.   The nature of the questions it is useful to ask depends, of course, on the means available for answering them. In recent years chemical and physical tools of great power have been developed and it is natural that, having these tools, we should think of explaining the behaviour of living things in terms of the chemist's molecules, now made visible by means of the refined methods of the physicists.

The most important kind of molecules we shall be concerned with are giant ones, especially those of proteins and nucleic acids.   In the next chapter some of the problems of molecular biology will be introduced by discussing the nature and biological role of the proteins.

2

Inside the Cell

In the previous chapter we spoke of the revolutions in biology which have led to more and more penetrating studies of living organisms at progressively increasing degrees of magnification. We considered the whole organism, the cell, and finally the chemical reactions within the cell, which were compared to the processes going on in a factory. We said that molecular biology was concerned especially with the working of the cell at a molecular level, mentioning in passing two of the most important kinds of molecule in the cell, namely the proteins and the nucleic acids. We pointed out that both these molecules are giant ones containing thousands of atoms, unlike the molecules usually dealt with by chemists, which have only some tens of atoms in them; and we said that in biological systems generally it is the giant molecules which are particularly important. Indeed molecular biology owes its existence and its impact to its capacity to study such giant molecules with an understanding which the older techniques of chemistry were unable to achieve.

In the next three chapters we shall discuss one of the two most important kinds of giant biological molecules, the proteins, and we shall look at them at the molecular level. To do this we must inevitably think in terms of chemical formulae and models, and they will be complicated ones at that, simply because the molecules themselves are complicated. So we will begin by discussing these formulae and models, and what they mean to the chemists who use them.

Formulae should be thought of as symbols. They are not the substances which they represent, but are symbols for those substances, in fact abstractions from reality. They tell something to the trained mind of the chemist. They ring bells in his mind, and the more highly trained he is, the more bells they ring.

For example, let us take the formula for water, almost the simplest of all and familiar to everybody, H_2O. What does this mean? It means that we have a molecule composed of two hydrogen atoms and an oxygen atom. If one is a chemist, one immediately appreciates that the atoms of the water molecule are arranged as in Figure 3, that the angle between the H—O bond and the O—H bond is about 105°, and that the distances between the hydrogen atoms and the oxygen are both 0.96×10^{-8} cm., just under a hundred millionth of a centimetre. Of course we cannot prove these facts from first principles, as it were; they are simply part of the accumulated experience of chemists about the make-up of molecules—that experience which is called up to the mind of the chemist when he looks at the formula H_2O. Our drawing of the molecule in Figure 3 is clearly a better representation—a more in-

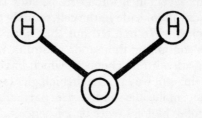

Fig. 3. Drawing of the molecule of water, H_2O.

formative symbol—than simply writing H_2O, but it is still not a completely adequate one. For we know that in fact an atom effectively occupies space. Even though modern physics has shown that all atoms are rather like miniature solar systems, with a cloud of negative electrons surrounding the tiny positively-charged nucleus, and are therefore largely 'empty', nevertheless two atoms cannot approach one another more closely than their electron clouds allow because of the electrical repulsion between these clouds. So in practice atoms often behave almost as if they were as solid as billiard balls, and a more realistic way of representing the water molecule would be the model shown in Plate 5, called a space-filling model. In it you can see the oxygen atom and the two hydrogen atoms represented by little coloured balls.

Yet another common form of representation is shown in Plate 6, which is of the so-called ball-and-spoke variety, in which the atoms have been deliberately reduced in size so that we can see the bonds between them. Every atom has a characteristic number of bonds from itself to its neighbours; chemists call these valency bonds. The advantage of using ball-and-spoke models is that, unlike the space-filling variety, they make it possible to see what the inside of a molecule is like, even when it is a complicated one. Ball-and-spoke models are therefore often used to illustrate the complicated molecules which we are concerned with in this book.

We have, then, four different methods of representing the water molecule, each of them being valuable in different circumstances.

Let us now go on to a slightly less simple example. CH_4 is the gas methane, one of the constituents of coal gas. To the chemist this formula means that its molecule consists of one carbon atom attached to four hydrogens. It might be

$$\begin{array}{c} H \\ | \\ \text{drawn thus} \quad H\!\!-\!\!C\!\!-\!\!H. \\ | \\ H \end{array}$$

But this representation is inade-

quate, for it is known that the four valency bonds from a carbon atom do not lie in a single plane as in this printed formula. In fact, they are directed towards the corners of a tetrahedron as shown in the model in Plate 7. This ball-and-spoke model gives a more realistic impression of what the molecule is like, simply because it is three-dimensional, which a printed formula can never be.

Suppose now that we remove one of the hydrogen atoms, leaving CH_3, and replace it by a second CH_3 group. We now have the molecule $CH_3 . CH_3$ or C_2H_6,

$$
\begin{array}{ccc}
\text{H} & \text{H} \\
| & | \\
\text{H--C--C--H,} \\
| & | \\
\text{H} & \text{H}
\end{array}
$$

which is also a gas, called ethane. And we can go on taking hydrogens off and adding CH_3 groups, thus building up by degrees a long chain of atoms, see Plate 8.

Carbon is more ready to build long chains than is any other kind of atom, and this is one of the reasons why carbon figures so largely in all the giant molecules we shall be considering in this book, and in living organisms generally. In the present example it can be seen that we arrive eventually at the general formula $CH_3 . CH_2 . CH_2 \ldots CH_3$. We can put on as many CH_2s as we like, and then terminate at the other end by a final CH_3, so that all the valency bonds are satisfied.

$$
\begin{array}{ccccc}
\text{H} & \text{H} & \text{H} & & \text{H} \\
| & | & | & & | \\
\text{H--C--C--C--} & \cdots\cdots & \text{--C--CH}_3 \\
| & | & | & & | \\
\text{H} & \text{H} & \text{H} & & \text{H}
\end{array}
$$

This series of molecules is known to chemists as the paraffins. If there is only one carbon atom, we have methane. If we go up to four, we have butane, which is commonly used as a fuel in gas cigarette lighters. Increase the number of carbon atoms to eight and the result is liquid octane, well known as a constituent of fuel for aeroplane and automobile engines, and so we go on until, when there is a large number of carbons in the molecule (say about twenty), we have heavy lubricating oil. Continue adding CH_2 groups and we come to greases like vaseline, and eventually to solids such as paraffin wax.

You will see that the molecules exhibit a regular gradation of properties as the number of carbon atoms increases: at first they are gases, then very volatile liquids, then more and more viscous liquids, and eventually solids.

This is the simplest possible example of a long chain molecule, or *polymer*, and it illustrates the way in which the properties progressively change as the molecule gets longer. There are plenty of other familiar examples; thus rubber and the synthetic plastics like nylon and terylene are all long chain molecules. And to come back to biology, nearly all the giant molecules we meet in living organisms are polymers. In particular, the proteins and the nucleic acids are built on this plan and, incidentally, so are the fats and the carbohydrates, though we shall not be concerned so much with these in this book. We might well ask ourselves *why* biological molecules are built like long chains, and this is a question we shall return to later.

Now large biological molecules, though made of a long chain of atoms, very often have the chain folded up so that the whole molecule has a nearly spherical shape. You can easily see that there must be very many different ways in which such a molecule might be folded. Our long chain molecule could be represented by a set of poppet beads (Plate 9a) which clip into one another to make a chain, and it is easy to understand that this could be folded into a solid lump in an infinity of ways (Plate 9b). Thus, even though in one sense the molecule is one-dimensional, to understand its structure fully we have to consider it as a three-dimensional object. We shall return to the three-dimensional aspect of long chain molecules in the next chapter. But for the moment let us introduce ourselves to the proteins by thinking of them in the first instance in their one-dimensional aspect.

In the paraffin chain the unit of construction, the *monomer* as it is called, was a methane molecule CH_4. In the proteins the monomers are molecules of a more complicated type, called by chemists amino acids; they are not all identical with one another, yet they have a close family resemblance. Figure 4 gives the formulae of a number of different amino acids and some models are shown in Plate 10.

It can be seen that one part of the molecule (shown at the top of each amino acid in Figure 4 and Plate 10) is the same in all the different amino acids. But the other part, shown projecting downwards and called the side chain, is different in every amino acid.

When amino acids link together they can do it as shown in Figure 5. Each amino acid loses at its left hand end a hydrogen

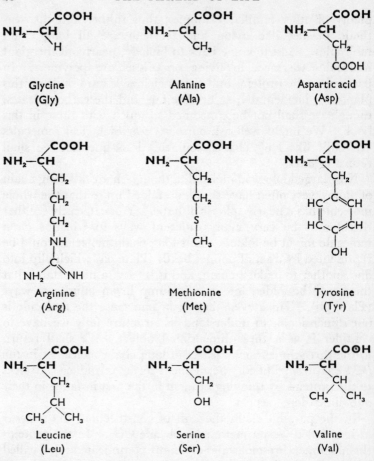

Fig. 4. The chemical formulae of some amino acids. In this and succeeding figures the amino acids are denoted by three-letter abbreviations, generally the first three letters of their names.

$$\text{NH}_2.\text{CH}.\text{CO}\boxed{\text{OH \quad H}}\text{NH}.\text{CH}.\text{CO}-\text{NH}.\text{CH}.\text{CO}-\text{NH}.\text{CH}.\text{CO}-\text{NH}.\text{CH}.\text{COOH}$$

Ala   Ser   Asp   Leu   Ala

Fig. 5. The formation of a polypeptide chain by elimination of a water molecule from the NH_2- and $-\text{COOH}$ groups of successive amino acids.

atom, and at its right hand end an OH group, and the free valencies 'hold hands', linking the amino acids together to form what is called a polypeptide chain; the H and OH go off to form a water molecule. You can see that the chain part, the *main chain* as it is called, repeats with every amino acid simply because it is built up from that part of the amino acids which is the same whatever the amino acid, but the successive *side chains* are different, being different for each type of amino acid. The scheme is rather like the charm bracelets girls wear. We can think of the bracelet as the main chain, and the charms as the side chains. A long bracelet of this kind might have quite a number of different kinds of charm, or side chain, on it. In the proteins there are twenty (and only twenty) different kinds of side chain, but a given type of side chain will generally appear more than once in a single protein molecule, which will normally contain hundreds of amino acids in all.

Thus we arrive at the conception of proteins as *polymers* of amino acids—polymers with very long chains, generally composed of hundreds of links.

So much for the chemist's picture of a protein molecule. Let us now consider why proteins are so very important in biology. Think once more of the cycle of chemical reactions in the yeast cell mentioned in the last chapter (Figure 2). The individual reactions, generally speaking, do not work in a test tube, or if they do work they go very slowly, much more slowly than they do in the living organism. This means that in the living organism there must be some agent which speeds up the reactions, makes them go faster than they would in a test tube. Such agents are *catalysts*, used to speed up reactions in living organisms just as in many industrial processes catalysts are used to speed up chemical reactions which would otherwise go too slowly. Many of the biological catalysts have been isolated by biochemists, and they are called *enzymes*. '*Enzyme*' comes from the Greek words ἐν ζύμη, meaning 'in yeast'. The name was chosen because the sequence of reactions in yeast which leads to the production of alcohol was one of the first to be studied by biochemists, and it turns out that there is a separate enzyme for each of the reactions in the sequence. So we have a dozen enzymes all concerned with this single chain of reactions. Moreover, each enzyme is highly specific; it will catalyse only its own particular reaction in the chain, and no other. Furthermore, it will only catalyse the reaction for the exact molecule for which it is designed; if the molecule is altered slightly it probably won't be affected by the enzyme at all.

Thus there are a dozen enzymes in this particular sequence of reactions; yet this represents only a small part of the total chemical activity of a yeast cell. In fact, almost every chemical reaction taking place in a cell is controlled by an enzyme. In a complete living cell there are something like a few thousand different sorts of enzyme, each one responsible for controlling its own particular chemical reaction and making it faster. So, in a very real sense, the enzymes are the 'works' of the living cell; in terms of our factory analogy they might be thought of as the machine tools of the cell. It will be clear from what has been said that they have an absolutely central importance. If we now add that every known enzyme has been shown to be a protein, it will be clear that one of our first tasks in trying to understand how living organisms work must be to understand how the proteins are constructed and how they function, either as enzymes or in other ways, in every living cell.

Many kinds of protein will already be familiar to the reader. Let us think of a few examples, first of all an enzyme. In the kitchen we use rennet to turn milk into junket. Rennet contains an enzyme called *rennin* which comes from the digestive apparatus of a calf and has the specific capacity of curdling milk. Another familiar protein is *keratin*; as we have already mentioned, hair is largely made of protein and keratin is the biochemist's name for this. In hair the protein is used for structural purposes, and indeed many other structural organs of the human body are made of protein; thus a major component of bone is a protein called *collagen*, while tendons and skin also consist mainly of protein.

Another example, to which we shall frequently return, is the protein called *haemoglobin*. This is the red colouring matter of blood. Its function is to carry oxygen from the lungs to the tissues, and haemoglobin has indeed a remarkable capacity for picking up molecules of oxygen. In fact, one haemoglobin molecule (Plate 24) can pick up four oxygen molecules simultaneously. It picks them up in the lungs where the oxygen pressure is high, carries them to the tissues where the oxygen pressure is low, and delivers them up. The oxygen thus brought to the tissues diffuses into the cell and it finds there another protein called *myoglobin* (Plate 23) which we shall also hear of again. Myoglobin is a kind of baby brother of haemoglobin, a molecule only a quarter the size and capable of picking up one oxygen molecule instead of four. It is also red; in fact it is responsible for making meat red in colour. The myoglobin picks up the oxygen from the haemoglobin and stores it until it is needed by the cell.

Another very important protein is *myosin* in muscle, a protein with the remarkable property of contractility; it is the fibres of myosin in the muscles which enable them to contract. How this trick is performed is one of the central and most challenging problems of biology, still far from completely solved.

As a final example, some of the hormones, the chemical messengers responsible for regulating bodily processes, are proteins—*insulin* for example.

So it can be seen that a vast variety of functions is performed by these protein molecules, although they are all made up of the same building blocks—the twenty different kinds of amino acid. The same building blocks in different combinations can produce molecules having all sorts of different properties and functions. It may seem remarkable that so large a variety of function can be based on as few as twenty different kinds of unit; but really it is no more surprising than the fact that the same twenty-six letters of the alphabet can be used to convey messages as diverse as a Shakespeare sonnet and a book about molecular biology.

In general, proteins consist almost entirely of amino acids, but it should be mentioned in parenthesis that some also contain a small additional group of some other type. For example, haemoglobin and myoglobin contain flat groups of atoms with an iron atom in the middle (Figure 6) called haem groups, and it is at the iron atom of the haem group that the oxygen molecule becomes attached. Haemoglobin contains four such groups and myoglobin only one.

The proteins have a role in living cells so central, so important, that it is not too much to say that the nature of any living cell is determined primarily by the proteins it contains, and hence that the nature of a complete living organism is in the final analysis determined by its proteins.

So to understand the nature and the functioning of the organism we must try to understand the nature and the functioning of the proteins in its cells. And to understand the

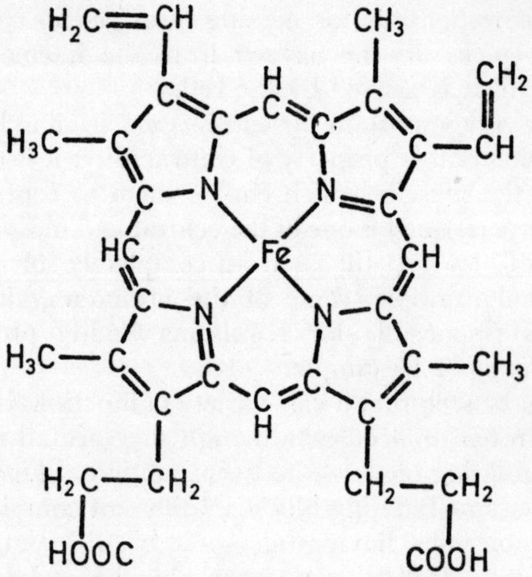

Fig. 6. The haem group. This flat group of atoms, with an iron atom (Fe) at its centre, is a component of the molecules of haemoglobin and myoglobin. The iron atom is the point of attachment of an oxygen molecule.

relations between different organisms we must understand the relations between the proteins they contain. This brings us to the problem of the species specificity of proteins; by which we mean that every species of organism has its own specific types of protein molecule, the same in each individual member of the species; but proteins having the same function in different species are not identical.

Thus, practically everyone reading this book contains

identically the same kind of haemoglobin molecules in his or her blood, identical down to the last amino acid and the last atom. Very occasionally an abnormal haemoglobin is found in human beings, but generally such abnormal haemoglobins produce very serious diseases, sickle cell anaemia for example. Nevertheless the molecular abnormalities in the haemoglobins seem very trivial; thus in sickle cell anaemia only two out of nearly six hundred amino acids contained in each haemo-globin molecule are changed. This is why I can be sure that virtually all my readers have identically the same haemo-globins—anyone having a different haemoglobin would be seriously ill or dead, because only the very slightest changes can be tolerated by the organism.

If we now turn to other species and look, for example, at the haemoglobin of a horse or a cow, these would be recogniz-ably very similar molecules. They would have the same colour, they would be performing the same functions, their molecules would be about the same size. However, a sensitive chemical analysis would show that characteristically there is a difference between horse haemoglobin, cow haemoglobin, and human haemoglobin—their tallies of amino acids are different. This is what we mean by species specificity and, indeed, it may turn out that the most meaningful basis for the classification of plants and animals is in terms of the differences between their proteins, rather than in terms of the external characteristics, such as colours, shape and so on, which Linnaeus had no option but to use.

In the next chapter we shall discuss the chemistry of protein molecules, that is to say the number and the kind of amino acids making them up, the order in which these are disposed along the polypeptide chain, and the ways which chemists have developed for investigating these so-called amino-acid sequences in different proteins. We shall see, however, that knowledge of the sequence alone is insufficient; in order to understand the function of a protein it is necessary to discover how its polypeptide chains are folded to form a solid object. And we shall see, too, how the physicists have come to the rescue of the chemists by providing a technique for studying large molecules in three dimensions instead of only in one.

c

3

Proteins in One Dimension, and How to Study Molecules in Space

IN the previous chapter we discussed the chemical make-up of protein molecules. We showed that their plan of construction is rather like that of the paraffin family or the synthetic polymers, in that they consist of long chains of units, or monomers, which in proteins are called amino acids. We showed, too, that there are twenty different kinds of amino acids in proteins, giving us twenty different sorts of side chain sticking out from the main chain of the molecule. We arrived at the concept of proteins as being *the* essential components of living organisms, or, if you like, the machine tools of the factory which is the living cell.

Perhaps this way of thinking about proteins may be unfamiliar to many people, who are used to the word protein mainly in connexion with their diet, and juggle the ratios of protein, fat and carbohydrate in the hope of producing what they conceive to be a currently fashionable silhouette. It is certainly true that proteins are very important as food, and, in fact, what happens when proteins are digested is that they are attacked by enzymes in the stomach juices and broken down into their individual amino acids; of course, these enzymes

34

are proteins too; so it is a case of dog eating dog. The individual amino acids are absorbed by the organism and, among other purposes, are used as a kind of pool on which it can draw in constructing its own proteins. Enzymes, then, play a very important part in digesting proteins and, as we shall very soon see, these same digestive enzymes are important also in studying proteins in the laboratory. One stomach enzyme, rennin, has already been mentioned, and others, such as pepsin, trypsin and chymotrypsin, which are found in human beings as well as other animals, are also very important to biochemists.

Let us return to the chemistry of proteins. If we think of a protein molecule as being made up of long polypeptide chains, the first questions which naturally occur to us are 'How many chains are there in the molecule?' and 'What is the order of the amino acids in each of those chains?'.

Biochemists have developed techniques to enable us to answer questions like these. For example, in order to count the number of chains in the molecule they use the so-called *end-group method*. The essence of this is to combine the protein with a coloured dye molecule which hooks on to one end of each chain—and which does not hook on anywhere else.* Having attached dye to the end of each chain the next step is to break down the protein into its individual amino acids—this is a very simple operation and happens, for example, if we just boil the protein with acid. The result is a mixture of amino acids in which those that were originally at the end of a chain are marked with the coloured dye. All we need to do now is to separate these coloured amino-acid derivatives from the rest and count them. For this purpose a method is used which has become enormously important in all branches of biochemistry, the technique known as chromatography.

You can easily do a little experiment in chromatography yourself. Put a spot of ink on a long piece of blotting paper, near one end, and then dip that end of the blotting paper into water so that the paper is vertical and the spot of ink is just

---

* In the particular method I am describing the dye will in fact also hook on to certain side chains not at the end of the polypeptide chain, but in practice this complication can easily be dealt with.

above the surface of the water. Then as the water soaks up into the blotting paper, it will carry the dyes in the ink up the paper with it. You will find that most inks contain a mixture of dyes, and that these travel at different rates in the paper, and so they appear after a while as distinct coloured bands at different levels on the blotting-paper strip.

This experiment is a very simple way of separating the dyes in the ink, and it is a very crude application of the chromatographic techniques which are now used for all sorts of purposes in biochemistry, and which with time have become very sophisticated and very complicated (see Plate 11). In the present connexion chromatography is used to separate and count the amino acids marked with the yellow dye, and hence to count the chains. It turns out that most proteins in fact consist of a small number of chains—perhaps only one, perhaps two or three or four; never a large number.

We come now to our second question: what is the order of amino acids along the chains? How in other words, can we determine the *amino-acid sequence* of the protein? The first step is to chop the chain into short lengths, known as peptides, using enzymes for the purpose. It has already been mentioned that enzymes are very specific—each enzyme will catalyse, or speed up, the rate of one particular reaction and no other. If, for example, we use one of the digestive enzymes called trypsin to break the protein into peptides, it makes a cut in the polypeptide chain only at those links which follow two particular side chains called lysine and arginine and nowhere else, as shown in Figure 7. So the result of this treatment is that the chain is split at every lysine and arginine, into short lengths each of which (except the last) must naturally terminate in lysine or arginine.

The next step is to separate the short lengths, or peptides, from one another, again by means of chromatography. After that we have to find a way of determining the sequence of amino acids in each peptide. This may be done by using another kind of enzyme, this time one which has the property of nibbling off amino acids one by one from the end of a peptide chain. Each time an amino acid is nibbled off, we identify it; by repeating the nibbling process again and again we can eventually, if we are lucky, write down the amino acid sequence of the whole peptide.

Finally, we have to decide the order in which the fragments were assembled in the original molecule. This is not so easy, and one of the best ways is to start all over again with a new sample of protein, and this time digest it with a different enzyme, say chymotrypsin, which chops the chain in different places, and gives us a different set of fragments overlapping the original set (Figure 7). By determining the amino-acid

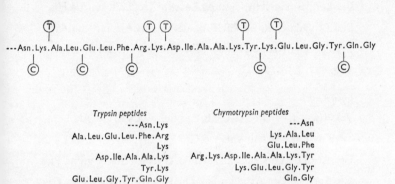

Fig. 7. The last 22 residues in the amino-acid sequence of myoglobin (of sperm whale), showing the points at which the chain is split by trypsin (T) and by chymotrypsin (C); also, the peptides resulting from tryptic and from chymotryptic splitting.

sequence of each of these new fragments, comparing these with the first set of fragments and looking for overlaps, we can if all goes well discover the original order in which both sets of peptides were assembled in the intact protein, and so piece this exceedingly complicated jigsaw puzzle together, thus eventually writing down the whole amino-acid sequence of the original molecule.

This process has been simply and briefly described in a few paragraphs, but in practice it is a very tedious and lengthy one. Even with small proteins it may take a single worker several years to determine a whole sequence. But it can be done—and indeed by now has been done for quite a number

Alpha chain

Val.Leu.Ser.Pro.Ala.Asp.Lys.Thr.Asn.Val.Lys.Ala.Ala.Try.

Gly.Lys.Val.Gly.Ala.His.Ala.Gly.Glu.Tyr.Gly.Ala.Glu.Ala.

Leu.Glu.Arg.Met.Phe.Leu.Ser.Phe.Pro.Thr.Thr.Lys.Thr.Tyr.

Phe.Pro.His.Phe.Asp.Leu.Ser.His.Gly.Ser.Ala.Gln.Val.Lys.

Gly.His.Gly.Lys.Lys.Val.Ala.Asp.Ala.Leu.Thr.Asn.Ala.Val.

Ala.His.Val.Asp.Asp.Met.Pro.Asn.Ala.Leu.Ser.Ala.Leu.Ser.

Asp.Leu.His.Ala.His.Lys.Leu.Arg.Val.Asp.Pro.Val.Asp.Phe.

Lys.Leu.Leu.Ser.His.Cys.Leu.Leu.Val.Thr.Leu.Ala.Ala.His.

Leu.Pro.Ala.Glu.Phe.Thr.Pro.Ala.Val.His.Ala.Ser.Leu.Asp.

Lys.Phe.Leu.Ala.Ser.Val.Ser.Thr.Val.Leu.Thr.Ser.Lys.Tyr.

Arg.

Beta chain

Val.His.Leu.Thr.Pro.Glu.Glu.Lys.Ser.Ala.Val.Thr.Ala.Leu.

Try.Gly.Lys.Val.Asn.Val.Asp.Glu.Val.Gly.Gly.Glu.Ala.Leu.

Gly.Arg.Leu.Leu.Val.Val.Tyr.Pro.Try.Thr.Gln.Arg.Phe.Phe.

Glu.Ser.Phe.Gly.Asp.Leu.Ser.Thr.Pro.Asp.Ala.Val.Met.Gly.

Asn.Pro.Lys.Val.Lys.Ala.His.Gly.Lys.Lys.Val.Leu.Gly.Ala.

Phe.Ser.Asp.Gly.Leu.Ala.His.Leu.Asp.Asn.Leu.Lys.Gly.Thr.

Phe.Ala.Thr.Leu.Ser.Glu.Leu.His.Cys.Asp.Lys.Leu.His.Val.

Asp.Pro.Glu.Asn.Phe.Arg.Leu.Leu.Gly.Asn.Val.Leu.Val.Cys.

Val.Leu.Ala.His.His.Phe.Gly.Lys.Gln.Phe.Thr.Pro.Pro.Val.

Gln.Ala.Ala.Tyr.Gln.Lys.Val.Val.Ala.Gly.Val.Ala.Asp.Ala.

Leu.Ala.His.Lys.Tyr.His.

Fig. 8. The amino-acid sequence of the alpha and beta chains of human haemoglobin. The complete molecule contains two alpha chains and two beta chains, and in addition four haem groups.

of proteins, though very few in comparison with all those which are important in the living cell.

Just to give a single example, Figure 8 shows the amino-acid sequence of human haemoglobin, a protein which we have already mentioned and to which we shall frequently refer again. The molecule of haemoglobin contains four polypeptide chains of two different kinds—two so-called alpha chains and two beta chains; in all there are 574 amino acids. Our figure gives the amino-acid sequences of each kind of chain, and shows just how complicated the chemical make-up of a typical protein is.

For some proteins, including the haemoglobins, the amino-acid sequence has been determined for a number of different species, and one finds that if, for example, one compares the amino-acid sequences of human and horse haemoglobins, for the most part the sequences are the same but every now and then there comes a difference. Broadly speaking, the farther apart the two animals lie in the evolutionary tree, the more differences there are found to be.

So much for amino-acid sequences. Thus far we have been talking about proteins as if they were one-dimensional structures, linear arrays of amino acids, as if they were completely described by their sequences of amino acids such as those in Figure 8. But in fact it can be shown that proteins are generally not one-dimensional at all. They are folded up, rolled into a kind of ball, nearly spherical in shape. Reverting to the notion of symbolism in chemical formulae, the amino-acid sequence of a protein is indeed a symbol for it, in fact a *unique* symbol (no two different proteins are known to have the same sequence), but it is by no means an *adequate* symbol if we are interested in the behaviour of the protein. It does not tell us how the chain is folded up. Nor does it tell us which side chains are close together and which ones are far apart in the folded molecule. It is easy to see that there are innumerable ways in which a polypeptide chain like the alpha chain of haemoglobin, with its 141 amino acid residues, *might* be folded up; the question is, which way is it *actually* folded up? On this question the amino-acid sequence as such throws no light. Again, in an enzyme, with its specific function of controlling a particular chemical change taking place in the cell, this specific function is mediated through a region on or near the surface of the molecule known as its active site. The 'active site' must be some kind of constellation, or group, of side chains which come together in the three-dimensional folded structure in just such a manner as to provide a shape to which the small molecule whose reaction is being controlled can fit—like a key into a lock. Clearly we cannot have any idea of the nature or action of this active site if we confine ourselves to the one-dimensional description. To understand protein function we must, therefore, go over into three dimensions. That is, our task must be to discover what the protein is like in space, as a three-dimensional object, and this is the problem to which we shall now address ourselves.

How can we determine the three-dimensional structure of an object so small as a protein molecule, less than a millionth of a centimetre across? It is no good looking at it with visible light, for the wavelength of visible light is very long compared with the dimensions of the molecule we want to study, much too coarse to reveal the details we are looking for. To show up these fine details within the molecule we must go to shorter wavelengths, smaller than the molecules themselves. What this means is that we must use X-rays, which are of exactly the same nature as light rays but have much shorter wavelengths —about as long as the distance between two neighbouring atoms in a molecule.

It is useless to look at a *single* molecule with X-rays; the molecule is so small that the reflections of the X-rays from it would be much too weak to detect. To get anything detectable we must use a large number of molecules for the X-rays to interact with. Furthermore, it is no good having a higgledy-piggledy arrangement of a large number of molecules as in a liquid or a gas, because then each one would reflect the X-rays in different directions, and all the individual contributions would overlap and simply give a kind of diffuse scattering of the X-ray beam.

We must, therefore, take an ordered arrangement of molecules in which they are all regularly lined up to face in the same direction—remember the analogy of soldiers on parade—so that when the X-ray beam hits them the reflections from each molecule go off in the same direction. The reflections from individual molecules then reinforce one another and we can record them on a photographic plate. Such an ordered arrangement of molecules is nothing else but a crystal, such as the crystal of common salt—sodium chloride—in Plate 12. We now know that the structure of this crystal is that illustrated by the model in Plate 13, in which the black circles and the empty circles represent the sodium atoms and the chlorine atoms respectively—a very simple structure with only two atoms in its molecule. If you fire a beam of X-rays at such a sodium chloride crystal and meanwhile expose a photographic plate behind it, you get the pattern of spots like that shown in Plate 14.

It was Sir Lawrence Bragg who, in 1913, first managed to unravel that pattern, called an X-ray diffraction pattern, and work back from it to the model, to the arrangement of the atoms in the crystal. He naturally started off with the simplest molecule he could find, with two atoms only, but as the years have gone by this method which he first devised has become more and more powerful, until now it can tackle crystals of molecules containing tens, hundreds or even thousands of atoms.

Let us take a simple example. Plate 15a shows a model of the structure of a fairly simple molecule, that of naphthalene. Plate 15b shows the map of naphthalene obtained by the X-ray crystallographer. It will be seen that they precisely correspond (Plate 15c). The second picture is referred to as a contour map because of the way the crystallographer expresses his results. X-rays are reflected by electrons, so by the X-ray method we are essentially investigating the distribution of electrons in the crystal. Thus the natural way for the crystallographer to express his results is to plot out the density of electrons at various points in the crystal; where there is much density there must be an atom, and where there is no density there are no atoms. So he plots his density in the form of contours just as the mapmaker plots the height of a mountain with contour lines, and every atom then shows up as an isolated mountain peak.

It turns out that it is quite easy—at any rate mathematically straightforward even if tedious in practice—to calculate from the structure of a crystal what X-ray pattern it would produce. In X-ray crystallography, of course, we have the reverse problem, of starting with the pattern and working back to the structure. This is not so easy, and it involves guesswork, or special 'tricks of the trade'. Since this is not a text-book on crystallography I will not go into these tricks of the trade, but simply ask my reader to assume that the puzzle can indeed be solved, and that even if guesswork is sometimes required, the correctness of the final solution can always be checked.

Now proteins, as well as simple substances like common salt, can be crystallized. Indeed, exceedingly nice crystals can be made from them (Plate 16). Just as the molecule of a protein is more complicated than that of common salt, so the X-ray pattern its crystal produces is more complicated. Plate 17 is actually an X-ray picture of a crystal of the protein myoglobin. The complete X-ray pattern of a protein has thousands and thousands of spots in it; indeed, this picture is only part of the complete X-ray pattern of a myoglobin crystal, which would contain something like 50,000 spots.

Can we disentangle that very complicated pattern and work our way back to the structure from which it is derived? To solve structures as complicated as this has become possible only in recent years, and very few have yet been unravelled.

In this chapter, then, I have described how we determine the number of polypeptide chains in a protein molecule, and the order of the amino acids along those chains. I have pointed out, however, that this knowledge is not enough—that to understand the functioning of proteins we must know their detailed three-dimensional structure. As we have seen, such structures can be solved by the methods of X-ray crystallography. The next chapter will describe what sort of objects these methods have revealed proteins to be.

4

Proteins in Three Dimensions

MOST of the previous chapter was devoted to thinking about proteins as one-dimensional objects, as long strings of amino acids, but towards the end I showed that this one-dimensional concept of protein structure is an inadequate one, that in order to understand the function of protein molecules and how they behave in the living cell it is necessary to think of them in three dimensions, and to determine their structures as solid objects. I also indicated that X-ray crystallography provided a direct method of studying molecules in three dimensions, and of discovering how the atoms in them are arranged in space.

I propose now to tell you something about the results of applying these X-ray methods to proteins. For a start let us go back to the first protein we encountered in this book, namely keratin, the principal component of hair. The X-ray photograph of it in Plate 1 is a very diffuse one, too messy for its structure to be determined by ordinary methods, and in fact this pattern was studied for very many years without the right solution being found. In the end the puzzle was solved by Pauling, by trial and error. Figure 1 (p. 15) shows a sketch of the structure, which is known as the alpha helix. You can see that in it the main chain is twisted into a kind of spiral, or more precisely a helix, like a corkscrew. The successive turns of the helix are held together by rather weak bonds, of the type known to chemists as hydrogen bonds, and these hydrogen bonds are represented in the figure by dotted lines. The side chains

stick out radially from the helix. In order to make the arrangement simpler to understand, the side chains are represented in
the picture by the same symbol, R; in other words they are
shown as if every amino acid in the chain was, say, alanine, the side
chain which consists simply of a $-CH_3$ group. In the real
protein, of course, the side chains would not all be alike because
as we have seen the amino-acid sequence of proteins is in
reality an apparently random arrangement of *different* side
chains.

The alpha helix has turned out to be the prototype of a
large number of different kinds of helical structure found in
biological systems. The alpha helix we can describe as a
single helix; it is a single strand like an extensible telephone
cord. In other kinds of molecule *double* or *triple* helices are
found. For example, the protein collagen which is found in
bone and in tendon has a structure in which there are three
chains twisted together like a triple electric light flex. We shall
meet other helices, in nucleic acid and in viruses, later in the
book; deoxyribonucleic acid (DNA), for example, forms
a double helix.

On reflection it is not surprising that the helix is a general
structural pattern for long chain molecules, synthetic as well as
biological. If you try to arrange a linked chain of similar
but unsymmetrically-shaped objects in a regular, repetitive
manner, so that the relation between each object and its
neighbours is the same all along the chain, then you will find
that inevitably you build a helix—you really have no option;
even the limiting case of a set of objects stretched out in a straight
line can be thought of as a degenerate helix.

The nature of the alpha helix makes it possible to give a
very satisfying interpretation of the stretching of hair or wool,
which of course is just a kind of hair too. If you dampen a hair
you can stretch it to twice its normal length, and under suitable
conditions it can be made to go back again to its original un-
stretched length. This behaviour is quite unlike that of most
kinds of fibres, which simply break if they are stretched very
much. Now this special property of hair can easily be understood in molecular terms, as was first demonstrated by Astbury
thirty years ago. Successive turns of the helix are held together

by weak bonds. When the hair is stretched, these bonds simply break, and the polypeptide chain can then be pulled out, like a telephone cord, and after being fully stretched it is about twice the length it was before. Incidentally, the phenomenon of 'permanent set' in hair (important in so-called permanent waving) is simply the process which stabilizes a stretched, or partially stretched, configuration by making strong cross bonds from each chain molecule to its neighbours, so that their configuration is firmly fixed—they can no longer coil or uncoil.

Thus the alpha helix is very important in helping us to understand the behaviour of hair. But in fact the alpha helix is not only important in the fibrous proteins. It turns out also to be a principal element in the structure of the so-called globular proteins, those in which the chains are folded up so that the molecules are nearly spherical in shape. This very important class of protein includes all the enzymes, as well as haemoglobin and myoglobin and many others.

We shall now consider the structure of one of these globular proteins, namely myoglobin, in which the arrangement in space of all the atoms has now been determined almost completely. You will remember that we spoke of two related proteins, haemoglobin and myoglobin, which contain iron and have the power of combining with oxygen, haemoglobin in blood and myoglobin in muscle cells.

Though it contains some 2500 atoms, myoglobin has a rather small molecule as proteins go. It consists of 153 amino-acids, strung together in a single long polypeptide chain. Attached to the chain is the haem group (Figure 6, p. 32), a flat group of atoms with an iron atom at its centre, and it is to this iron atom that the oxygen molecule is attached.

The X-ray photograph of a myoglobin crystal shown in Plate 17 is much sharper and contains much more detail than the photograph of hair in Plate 1. The myoglobin pattern has in all about 50,000 reflections in it. (They cannot all be seen in the picture, which only shows part of the pattern.) In order to solve the structure completely, we have to measure up all these thousands of spots—a very tedious business. After that, lengthy calculations have to be made, using all these measurements; a formidable computing problem for which it is necessary to make use of the largest high-speed computers available.

In actual practice the structure of myoglobin was solved in successive stages, starting with a small number of reflections, only a few hundreds; these give what is called a *low resolution* picture of the molecule. This is equivalent to looking at the molecule through a rather inadequate pair of spectacles, so that one sees simply a fuzzy outline of the polypeptide chain and not the individual atoms of which it is composed.

Plate 18 shows a contour map of the low resolution model of the molecule. You will see that this is very much like the contour map in Plate 15, but because we are looking at a *three-dimensional* object we now have to draw a *three-dimensional* contour map. This is done by cutting a series of equidistant parallel sections though the molecules and plotting the density in each section as a set of contours; the sheets are then stacked on top of one another to give us a representation of the distribution of density in space. As will be seen, the resulting three-dimensional map is at first sight very complicated— but on close examination it is possible to trace through it a dense rod, winding here and there irregularly. This turns out to be simply the polypeptide chain—with our weak pair of spectacles the individual atoms in the chain cannot of course be seen, and they fuse together to give a rod of high density. Besides the polypeptide chain one can also make out the iron atom as a very dense mass. It shows up because it is a very heavy atom, much more dense than any other in the molecule.

Starting with this contour map we can make a model (Plate 19) of what the molecule must be like. The polypeptide chain can be followed right round it and you can also see the haem group containing the iron atom. One might perhaps have expected that the main chain would have been arranged in some regular symmetrical manner; the most striking feature of the model, however, is that the arrangement seems to be completely irregular and unsymmetrical.

Naturally, once one has obtained a model like this, one is impatient to increase its resolution—to look at the molecule with sharper spectacles—in hopes of seeing the individual atoms in it. But this meant measuring up very many more reflections, ten or twenty thousand of them, and carrying out calculations so elaborate that it would be impossible to have done them by hand. Very large, very fast electronic computers had to be used. The result was another three-dimensional contour map (Plate 20), much more complicated than the last one. A number of new features can be seen at a glance. If we look exactly along the length of one of the polypeptide chains we can see that what was a solid rod in the low resolution map has now developed a hole along its axis. In fact, looked at more closely, it turns out not to be a hollow cylinder, but actually a hollow helix—the chain spiralling round the central space. If the helix is measured up carefully it is found to be precisely our old friend the alpha helix, originally deduced as the structural basis of human hair and now showing up in the molecular structure of myoglobin, a very different kind of protein.

By studying the contour map in great detail (see Plate 21) one can arrive at a high resolution model of the whole molecule (Plate 22), pinpointing the position of each individual atom. Glance again at the low resolution model; the two models are viewed from the same angle in these pictures. What we have done is to take the flesh off the bones, as it were, so now we can see the atoms within the polypeptide chains, revealing the skeleton underlying the former shape. The high resolution model in Plate 22 is constructed a little differently from any we have met before. It is rather like the ball-and-spoke models, but this time the balls have been omitted and we are simply left with the spokes; we must imagine the atoms to be located at the intersections or ends of every spoke. The balls have been left out because the molecule we are looking at is so complicated that if they had been included the model would have been impossibly confusing. Even so it is quite hard to get an impression of the arrangement, especially in a two-dimensional photograph. To help the eye, the course of the main chain itself (mostly in the form of stretches of alpha helix, giving place to irregular segments where the chain turns a corner) has been indicated by a white cord. Also the iron atom, and the place where oxygen would go, have been indicated by little spheres.

The spoke model is a representation of the skeleton of the

molecule, but it does not perhaps give an adequate idea of what the molecule as a whole really looks like. Plate 23 shows another representation of the same molecule, this time made of space-filling atomic models. It is just the same structure again, but now the atoms are all made full-size —2500 of them. It is virtually a solid lump of atoms, and every atom has its own place in the structure. There is nothing accidental or random about it.

To understand this model is a challenge—and it is typical of the challenges confronting the molecular biologist. Can he explain how this complex molecule, containing 2500 atoms, performs its particular and special function in the living cell? Having a precise model of myoglobin, the biochemist can now set to work to try to explain just how it carries out its special trick of combining reversibly with oxygen. If he could explain this—and, incidentally, nobody has yet done so—then we would have the key to one of the most important physiological processes for which proteins are responsible.

Let us now take a look at haemoglobin, big brother of myoglobin, the protein of red blood cells. Whereas myoglobin has a single chain, haemoglobin has four, and in fact it is just about four times as big, containing some 10,000 atoms in all, and a total of 574 amino acids. It has four haem groups, four iron atoms, and combines with four oxygen molecules.

Because haemoglobin is bigger and more complicated than myoglobin, the analysis of its structure has not yet gone quite so far and up to now my colleague, Max Perutz, who is studying it, has only the low resolution model shown in Plate 24, which corresponds to the first, low resolution, model of myoglobin (Plate 19). It is quite hard to make sense of the model, but close examination reveals that there are four sub-units, two each of two different kinds. These are called the alpha chains (shown in white) and the beta chains (shown in black) and they correspond to the two kinds of chain, the sequences of which have been given in Figure 8. The whole assembly packs together into a compact, almost spherical shape.

The model can be taken to pieces (Plate 25), and if this is done the remarkable fact emerges that each kind of sub-unit, the alpha chain and the beta chain, has a remarkably close resemblance to the chain of myoglobin. This is very astonishing, because it so happens that the myoglobin and haemoglobin we have illustrated come from two entirely different animal species, the haemoglobin from a horse and the myoglobin from sperm whale. Here we have two different proteins found in different kinds of cell from two quite different animals, and yet the shapes of their molecules are nearly the same. So though this extraordinary shape is a very complicated and irregular one it is evident that it is by no means accidental—it must have some general significance, since it appears in different tissues and in widely different animals. We don't know yet what the significance is. But at least we have here two structures which the chemists can, so to speak, get their teeth into, when they try to explain protein *function* in terms of protein *structure*.

In fact, haemoglobin and myoglobin are the only two proteins whose structures have so far been determined, but there is no reason why the structures of many enzymes should not be determined in much the same way, and it should then be possible to study the active site of these enzymes and to explain in chemical terms how they speed up their own specific chemical reactions.*

In addition one ought to be able to understand from the structure what happens when incorrect amino acids are included in it. It has already been mentioned that this is what happens in the abnormal haemoglobins. In some of these the chemical abnormality consists simply of a single amino acid different from the usual in each of the alpha chains or beta chains. We may hope to explain how such a change alters the properties of the haemoglobin. For example, there is one particular kind of abnormal haemoglobin called haemoglobin M, in which the defect consists in a loss of the ability to combine reversibly with oxygen. If one studies with the

---

* Since this chapter was written I learnt the exciting news that the structure of a third protein, lysozyme, has been determined in atomic detail at the Royal Institution in London. Lysozyme is the first *enzyme* whose structure has been established, but this has been done so very recently that its mode of action is only now being examined. Other proteins are being studied in various laboratories all over the world and, in one or two cases, low resolution contour maps of their molecules have now been obtained.

D

haemoglobin model the position of the defective amino acid in haemoglobin M, one finds that it is very close to the iron atom of the haem group, in fact so close that it can probably hook directly on to the iron, thus occupying the position normally taken up by an oxygen molecule, and blocking the combination. This is a very satisfying explanation of why the loss of function occurs, and it was the first case in which we were able to get a direct correlation between the structure and a physiological abnormality in a protein molecule.

In this chapter we have discussed the nature of protein molecules as we understand them today, in chemical and structural terms. In the next chapter we shall address ourselves to a different question—how it is that protein molecules come into existence, how they are synthesized by the cell. How are particular proteins, different for every species of plant or animal, specified with great precision—down to the last atom—by the hereditary apparatus of each living cell? We must now turn, in other words, to a consideration of the mechanisms of genetics and heredity.

5
Reproduction and Genetics

In the preceding chapters we have been concerned with the molecular basis of the metabolism of cells—of that ceaseless chemical activity which is one of the hall-marks of life. Another distinguishing characteristic of living things, perhaps the most fundamental of all, is their ability to reproduce themselves; and in the chapters which follow we shall be considering what light has been thrown on this astonishing process by recent developments in biology.

Biological reproduction is of two kinds, asexual and sexual. Asexual reproduction occurs whenever cells divide, for example during the growth of any multi-cellular organism, and often when single-celled organisms reproduce themselves. Bacteria, for example, often use this method. The other method, sexual reproduction, involves the fusion of two cells, one derived from each parental organism, and it is familiar to us all in the fertilization of an egg by a spermatozoon. The two methods differ in many ways, but in either case we may, from our present point of view, think of the process in terms of the transfer of information. The parental cell (or cells) must pass information to a progeny cell to enable it to grow into its predetermined form by interaction with its environment. The *amount* of information which is passed must be enormous, since even a single cell is highly complicated and evidently requires the most elaborate and detailed instructions to enable it to build itself. Not only must the information be great in quantity, but also it must be highly *specific* in the literal sense of that word—for the essence of reproduction is that species breed true: the progeny of a man is always a man, and the progeny of a butterfly is always a butterfly.

Pursuing this train of thought we are immediately faced by questions like the following: where in the cell is the information, the blueprint, which is passed from one generation to another? How is it transferred from parent to progeny? How does it direct the building of new cells? Problems like these are among the most challenging in biology, and from the earliest times scientists and thinkers have proposed hypotheses of all sorts to account for the astonishing series of events which results in the development of an organism like man in all its complexity from a single fertilized egg cell. Some of the old biologists, for example, thought that every human spermatozoon contained a homunculus, a miniature replica of the human being that the sperm was destined to become (Plate 26). Nowadays biologists armed with much better tools, such as modern microscopes, are able to adopt a less speculative approach and base their theories on actual observation of the contents and behaviour of living cells.

The most prominent object in a cell is its *nucleus* (Plate 4), a dense central region demarcated from the surrounding cytoplasm. Biologists in their various studies of cells came to realize more and more clearly that the nucleus plays a key role; it is in some sense the control centre of the cell. Take the nucleus out of a cell by micromanipulation, and the activities of the cell cease; eventually it dies unless the nucleus is meanwhile put back again. In certain single-celled organisms you may even remove the nucleus from one variety of cell and replace it by a nucleus derived from another variety, whereupon the first cell promptly develops attributes characteristic of the second variety. It would appear, then, that the nucleus is essential to the continued activity of the cell, and further, that the characteristics of the cell are in some sense determined by the nucleus it contains. Our attention is inevitably focused on the nucleus as the control and information centre of the cell.

Let us now look at the photographs in Plate 27; they are a series of stills from a film of a dividing cell. Before the cell as a whole divides its nucleus splits into two daughter nuclei—and as a preliminary to the division of the nucleus it can be seen to acquire structure, to separate out into a bunch of assorted long, thin, irregular rods known as *chromosomes*. Each of the chromosomes is double stranded (Plate 27b), and as division occurs the two strands separate and migrate to opposite ends of the cell (Plate 27c), where two new nuclei are formed (Plate 27d) and eventually become part of the two daughter cells. Later each chromosome in the daughter nuclei duplicates itself, becoming double stranded in readiness for the next cell division. The net result is that every daughter cell contains a complete set of chromosomes corresponding precisely to the parental set.

It has gradually become clear that it is the chromosomes which carry the information, the blueprint, from one cell to its progeny and from one generation to the next. This conclusion is based on a great variety of experiments carried out with all sorts of different organisms. For example, during the last half century a vast deal of research has been done with the humble fruit fly, *Drosophila melanogaster*. This animal has been a favourite experimental subject among geneticists for a variety of reasons. It is very easy to grow; its generation cycle is very short so that a long sequence of generations can be studied in a conveniently brief space of time. The cells of *Drosophila* each contain a small number of chromosomes (different organisms have different chromosome numbers—in *Drosophila* it is 4 pairs, in man it is 23 pairs), and in some of its cells they are very large so that their details can be studied under the microscope. Our photograph (Plate 28) shows that the *Drosophila* chromosomes have characteristic sequences of light and dark bands along their lengths. Geneticists have been able to prove that visible characteristics of the organism are associated with particular regions of the chromosomes— changes in specific band-patterns are accompanied by defined changes in the appearance of the fly. This correspondence between points on the chromosomes and features of the external appearance of the organism—between genotype and phenotype as the geneticist would put it—can be expressed in the form of a so-called chromosome map, like that illustrated in Plate 29.

We thus arrive at the idea that the piece of hereditary information controlling a particular characteristic of the adult organism is located at a particular point on a particular chromosome. This information-packet is known as a *gene*, and we may, if we wish, regard a chromosome as being simply a string of genes. But how does the gene exercise its control? We have already become familiar in this book with the idea that the nature of a cell is determined by the nature of the enzymes and other proteins which it contains. It will not come as a surprise, therefore, that the hypothesis which seems best to fit the facts is that genes exercise control by directing the synthesis of enzymes (and other proteins); if a gene changes for some reason or another, then the protein whose synthesis it directs will change too. This is the famous 'one gene—one enzyme' hypothesis: it states that every gene is responsible for directing the synthesis of its own particular enzyme and that the control of the phenotype by the genotype is exercised as a control of enzyme structure by individual genes.

So far we have discussed the problems of genetics in terms of objects which we can actually see in the microscope. As molecular biologists we are not content with this—our object is to understand the behaviour of living organisms in terms of molecules—and our next question must be: what kind of an object is a gene at the molecular level?

If indeed the gene can be thought of in these terms, then the molecule we are looking for must have several quite distinctive and remarkable characteristics. First, it must be capable of self-reproduction with a remarkable degree of accuracy, though not with absolute perfection—indeed, it is just the occasional imperfections in the self-reproduction of the gene, known as mutations, which lead to variability in animals and plants and so eventually to the development of new species. Secondly, our molecule must act as a repository of information. Thirdly, it must be capable of using its information store, directly or indirectly, to control the production of enzymes, just as a piece of telegraph tape fed into a teleprinter produces a written message. This, then, is the very exacting specification of the molecule we are seeking.

Since genes are part of the chromosomes, we might for a

start enquire about the chemical make-up of chromosomes. Chemists have shown that they are principally composed of protein and of nucleic acid, so these would appear to be the promising candidates for our self-reproducing information store. We have already discussed the chemistry of proteins, but we have not yet had any dealings with nucleic acids, so I propose now to spend a little time telling you about them.

First of all, nucleic acids, like proteins, are very large molecules; indeed they are often much larger than proteins. Secondly, and again like proteins, nucleic acids are long chain molecules. But here the resemblance ends, for the links of nucleic acid chains, the so-called *nucleotides*, are quite unlike the amino-acid links of the proteins; each is made up of three different constituents, namely a sugar molecule, a phosphate group, and a rather complicated group which chemists called a base; the base may either be a purine base or a pyrimidine base, to give them their chemical names. Figure 9 (p. 59) is the chemists' symbolic formula of a length of nucleic acid chain. There are several different kinds of nucleic acid, and that illustrated here is the one found in chromosomes; its full chemical name, deoxyribonucleic acid, is most unwieldy and it is nearly always referred to by a shorthand title, namely DNA. Phosphate groups and sugar molecules are strung together alternately to form the main chain, and sticking out at the sides are the purine and pyrimidine bases. The purine bases are of two kinds, adenine and guanine; there are also two kinds of pyrimidines, called cytosine and thymine. It is not necessary to remember all these new names; we might just as well refer to the four kinds of base by the initial letters of their names, A, G, C and T. And all we need notice about their structures is that the purines (A and G) are large, with molecules containing two rings of atoms, while the pyrimidines (C and T) are small, containing only a single ring.

Chemists used to find nucleic acids extremely difficult to handle and to analyse. They are not easy to purify; their molecules are so long that they may actually break into pieces when a solution of them is stirred. And because single nucleic acid molecules may contain thousands or millions of atoms it is very hard to analyse them accurately. Indeed, methods for the chemical analysis of nucleic acids were only properly worked out quite recently, and the earlier analyses were quite far from the truth—when I was at school we were taught that the four bases were present in equal quantities, in 1 : 1 : 1 : 1 ratios, but in the last fifteen years it has become clear that this is by no means the case.

Certainly in those early times (and when one is talking about molecular biology the 1930s seem like prehistory) DNA did not seem to be a very good claimant to the title of biological information carrier. The original analyses made it seem a rather dull molecule, with the four bases present in equal quantities and presumably repeating along the chain in invariant sequence (as indicated in Figure 9). Most people thought the DNA was simply some kind of scaffolding—a support for the chromosomal protein. As an information carrier, protein appeared to be a much better candidate—its continuously varying sequence of twenty different kinds of amino acid seemed admirably suited to be some kind of code which could act as an information store.

Ideas of this kind, which were held by most biologists, received a rude shock in consequence of some experiments carried out as recently as the middle forties on a strange phenomenon known as bacterial transformation. These experiments showed that the heredity of certain micro-organisms, especially the bacterium *Pneumococcus* which causes pneumonia, could be permanently altered by DNA. What was done was to extract pure nucleic acid from a particular strain of *Pneumococcus*, call it strain A, and to allow it to interact with cells of *Pneumococcus* of a different strain, B. Thereupon the DNA from strain A enters the bacteria of strain B and, lo and behold, the progeny of these strain B bacteria, and their progeny in turn, are found to have been converted to strain A. In other words, the hereditary characteristics of an organism have been permanently altered by injecting into it chemically pure foreign DNA—and this is the important point—without any admixture of protein. It follows, therefore, that at least in bacteria it must be DNA which is responsible for carrying hereditary information. All later work has indicated that the same is generally true of all other kinds of organism; DNA is the information carrier of living cells.*

This remarkable experiment, and other similar ones, focused a great deal of attention on DNA. Not least it aroused the interest of two colleagues of mine, Jim Watson and Francis Crick, and just as the focusing of the sun's rays may cause a conflagration, so too this focusing of attention rapidly produced a conflagration which during the last decade has transformed the whole of biology.

We have seen in this chapter how biologists came to discover that nucleic acids were the information carriers of living cells, the repositories of the blueprint which has to be passed on from generation to generation, from parental cell to progeny cell. Once this was realized it became enormously important to investigate the structure of nucleic acids, as a preliminary to understanding how they could perform the three functions implicit in their key biological role: the function of reproducing themselves, that is replication; the function of acting as a store of information; and the function of using their information store in directing the growth of a new cell.

* In some viruses the hereditary information is carried by a different kind of nucleic acid, ribonucleic acid, or RNA.

6

Nucleic Acid—Molecule of Heredity

In Chapter 5 we saw that the hereditary information, which is carried by every cell and passed on from one generation to the next, is actually located on the chromosomes in the cell nucleus. The small packets of information, each of which is responsible for the synthesis of a single protein, are called genes. Chromosomes are made up of protein and nucleic acid (or DNA), but it is the DNA which actually carries the information. We looked at the chemical formula of DNA (Figure 9); it is a long chain of alternate sugar and phosphate groups, and to each sugar group is attached a side chain which may be one of four different kinds of base. Just as the chemical formula of a protein (Figure 5) does not get us very far towards an understanding of protein function, so the chemical formula of nucleic acid is inadequate as a symbol; it does not on the face of it give us any clues as to how DNA could replicate itself or store information.

As in the other examples we have considered, it is natural at this point to ask how the atoms in the DNA molecule are arranged in space; and once again we turn for help to X-ray crystallography. Purified DNA can be drawn out into fibres, in which the long thin molecules are all lined up like the stalks in a bundle of straw. The arrangement is then not unlike the arrangement of long thin keratin molecules in a hair, and if a

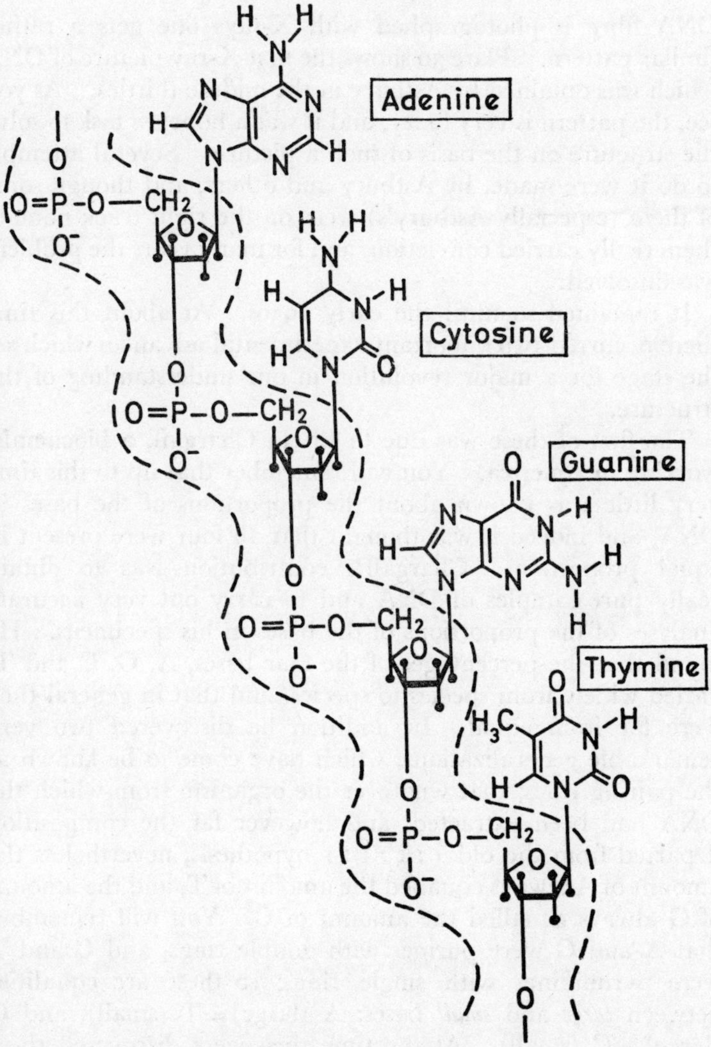

Fig. 9. The formula of a single strand of deoxyribonucleic acid (DNA). The main chain, or backbone, is enclosed between wavy lines and would extend a very long way above and below the diagram. The side chains project to the right; the four different kinds are shown, but in reality these would be arranged in an irregular sequence along the chain.

After Watson, J. D. (1965), in Molecular Biology of the Gene, *p. 91. New York: Benjamin, Inc.*

DNA fibre is photographed with X-rays one gets a rather similar pattern. Plate 30 shows the first X-ray picture of DNA which was obtained by Astbury in the middle thirties. As you see, the pattern is very fuzzy, and it was a hopeless task to solve the structure on the basis of such a picture. Several attempts to do it were made, by Astbury and others, and though some of them (especially Astbury's) were on the right track none of them really carried conviction, and for many years the problem was unsolved.

It remained so until the early 1950s. At about this time there occurred two important experimental advances which set the stage for a major revolution in our understanding of the structure.

The first of these was due to Erwin Chargaff, a biochemist working in America. You will remember that up to this time very little was known about the proportions of the bases in DNA, and indeed it was thought that all four were present in equal proportions. Chargaff's contribution was to obtain really pure samples of DNA and to carry out very accurate analyses of the proportions of the bases in his specimens. He found that the percentages of the four bases, A, G, C and T, varied widely from species to species, and that in general they were far from equal. In addition he discovered two very remarkable generalizations, which have come to be known as the pairing rules; that whatever the organism from which the DNA had been extracted, and however far the composition departed from the old 1 : 1 : 1 : 1 hypothesis, nevertheless the amount of A always equalled the amount of T, and the amount of G always equalled the amount of C. You will remember that A and G were purines with double rings, and C and T were pyrimidines with single rings; so these are equalities between *large* and *small* bases: A (large) = T (small), and G (large) = C (small). At the time they were discovered these generalizations were inexplicable, but in the event they provided one of the principal clues to solving the structure of DNA.

The other important experimental advance was made by two British workers, Maurice Wilkins and Rosalind Franklin, and their collaborators. They were able to make vast improvements in the quality of X-ray photographs obtainable from a DNA fibre, as you will readily see by comparing a modern picture (Plate 31) with the original Astbury photograph (Plate 30). The resemblance between the two photographs is unmistakable, but the new pictures contained a large number of rather sharp spots instead of fuzzy smears, and to a crystallographer they really looked for the first time as if something might be made of them.

These, then, were the new experimental facts, and the people who took advantage of them were two colleagues of mine, Jim Watson and Francis Crick. Jim Watson was a young American, aged only 24 at the time (1953), who had come to work with me in our laboratory at Cambridge on protein structure. It was my loss, but a great good fortune for biology, that Jim really did not take to the protein field—as he was the first to admit, it was too much like hard work for him—and instead of continuing in it he began to talk to Francis Crick, who was already in our laboratory, about the importance of solving the structure of DNA. They looked at the new X-ray photographs, they wondered about Chargaff's base pairing rules, they tried out all sorts of models, and the upshot was that in only a few weeks, after one or two false starts, they actually solved the whole thing! I would find it very hard to explain just how they did solve it—indeed, I think they would find it hard too. It is a good example of one of those intuitive jumps which happens in science from time to time. You may call it genius, you may call it inspiration, or what you will. One thing is clear, that the jump could not have been made earlier than 1953, because it absolutely depended upon a knowledge of the base-pairing rules and of the information contained in the improved X-ray photographs. But once these had become available it became possible to find the answer in a remarkably short time.

Plate 32 shows a ball-and-spoke model of the DNA structure of Watson and Crick. It is a double helix—there are two DNA strands in the molecule, as can be seen in the model; these run in opposite directions, and they are twisted together just like the two wires in an electric light flex. The result is a structure rather like a spiral staircase. The steps of the spiral staircase are in fact pairs of DNA bases, hooked together by the same type of weak chemical bonds, hydrogen bonds, as we have already met in the alpha helix of proteins. The essence of the structure is that each step consists of a pair of bases, one big and one small, and a step can be either an A—T pair, or it can be a G—C pair. You could not have two of the small bases in a step, T and C, T and T, or C and C, because they would not meet in the middle. You could not have two big ones, A and G, A and A, or G and G, because there would not be enough room for them. Similarly, you cannot mate together A and C, or G and T, simply because the chemical structures of these bases are such that in these combinations the hydrogen bonds would not pair off properly. So the structure gives a ready-made explanation of the Chargaff pairing rules: every step is either an A—T pair or a G—C pair, and therefore in the whole molecule the sum total of A's must equal the sum total of T's, and the total of G's must be equal to the total of C's. And this explanation is so neat, that to anyone who looks at the structure in detail, especially if he does so with the eye of a crystallographer or a structural chemist, it carries a kind of absolute conviction. You feel that this just simply has to be right.

Of course, once you have a model like the Watson-Crick double helix you can proceed to test it rigorously. You can calculate what X-ray pattern it should have, and see how the calculated pattern corresponds with what we actually observe, namely the X-ray photograph shown in Plate 31. Watson and Crick, by a process of trial and error, modified their model slightly until the fit with the observed X-ray pattern was quite satisfactory, and since then Wilkins has refined it further, and now the fit is extraordinarily good. But none of the later modifications have altered the grand simplicity of the original Watson and Crick structure. The structure has been confirmed in detail, and we can be absolutely certain that in a fibre of DNA the chains are arranged in this manner.

DNA in a fibre, however, is not necessarily the same thing as a DNA molecule in a living cell; it cannot simply be assumed that the structure unambiguously demonstrated to be present in the fibre also represents the state of a DNA molecule in its biological environment. However, during the past few years many biochemists and physical chemists have studied DNA, as it exists in the living cell, by a variety of techniques which we have no space to go into here, and they have shown that in the living cell, too, DNA is normally present as a double helix.

Nowadays, we can even look at a single DNA molecule directly, under the electron microscope. Plate 33 shows a short section of a single molecule, about two ten-millionths of a centimetre across. As we shall see in the sequel, this is indeed the thread of life. The first question to ask about it is how it performs its primary function, which is to replicate— how it is ensured that, when a cell divides, the DNA in each daughter cell is identical with the DNA of the parental cell? Watson and Crick proposed a very bold and simple hypothesis. They suggested that the DNA helix unwinds into two separate single strands, and that a new strand forms up alongside each single strand from nucleotides lying loose in the cell, the bases pairing up according to the Chargaff rules. It is easy to see that the result is two new double helices, identical with each other and with the original double helix (see Figure 10). The process can be likened to the preparation of a positive print from a negative in photography, although with the difference that in DNA there is no distinction in kind between the two strands—each can be thought of as the 'negative' of the other. In more recent times it has even been possible to make direct photographs in the electron microscope of DNA molecules in the act of replicating (Plate 34).

That, then, was the hypothesis. But biologists could see all sorts of difficulties about it, above all because DNA molecules are of enormous length. The total DNA in a single human cell, distributed over 46 chromosomes, contains something like a thousand million base pairs, and its actual length is about three feet. Indeed, all the DNA in a single human being would reach right across the solar system. Somehow three feet of it must be wrapped up into a single cell perhaps a thousandth of an inch across, and if the Watson-Crick hypothesis is correct all that DNA has to unwind during each act of replication. Anyone who has ever tried to separate the two strands of a long electric light flex will understand why biologists found it difficult to understand how this could happen without the whole thing getting into a hopeless tangle.

So it was very important to devise some kind of crucial experiment which would test the hypothesis. This was done, and carried through completely successfully, by Meselson and

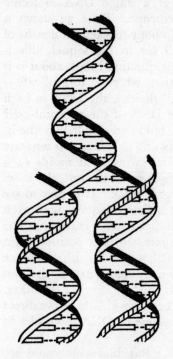

Fig. 10. The Watson-Crick scheme for the replication of DNA. The double helix (*above*) unwinds, and as it does so new DNA strands are formed on each of the original strands (*below*), the base-pairing rules ensuring that each new double helix has the same complementary base sequence as the original one.

After Watson, J. D. (1965), in Molecular Biology of the Gene, *p. 267. New York: Benjamin, Inc.*

Stahl. What they did was to grow some bacteria in a synthetic medium containing heavy nitrogen, that is to say an isotope of nitrogen heavier than the normal one (nitrogen 15 instead of nitrogen 14). After the bacteria had been grown in this medium all the nitrogen in their DNA bases was of the heavy type, and it could be calculated that the density of this DNA should be nearly one per cent. higher than the normal density of DNA. Having thus grown bacteria containing heavy DNA, Meselson and Stahl transferred them to a medium containing ordinary light nitrogen (nitrogen 14) and allowed the bacteria to divide, to reproduce themselves, making use of light nitrogen to synthesize new DNA; they then extracted the DNA from the progeny.   Figure 11 shows that if the Watson-

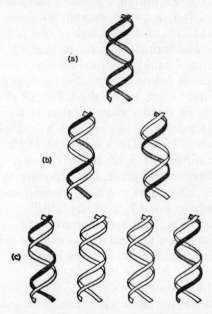

Fig. 11. Successive generations in the replication of heavy DNA in a light medium. (a) Parent molecule with two heavy strands, (b) first-generation daughter molecules, each with one heavy and one light strand, (c) second-generation daughter molecules, two with one heavy and one light strand, two with both strands light. *Meselson, M., & Stahl, F. W.* Proc. Nat. Acad. Sci., Wash., 44, 671 (1958).

Crick theory is right the first generation offspring should contain a medium-heavy DNA, less dense than the heavy DNA we started with but more dense than normal DNA, because it would all consist of one heavy strand and one light strand.   It should be, say, half per cent. or so above the normal density.   The diagram also shows that if we go on to a second generation, we must expect to find two different kinds of DNA in the extract.   Some of it should be DNA of normal density, made up of two light strands, and some of it should be medium-heavy DNA, made up of one light and one heavy strand.

That is what the theory would predict. How can prediction be checked? It means finding a sensitive method of measuring the density of DNA, sensitive enough to show a difference between normal DNA, and DNA half or one per cent. heavier than normal. The principle used is that of the gradient column, a column of liquid of graded density—less dense at the top and more dense below. Any object dropped into such a column will come to rest under the influence of gravity at a height such that its density matches that of the liquid in its immediate neighbourhood. By using this principle we should be able to separate heavy DNA and light DNA—they would come to rest at different heights in the column. But because the density differences are small, it is necessary to increase the sensitivity of the method as much as possible; and in practice the graded density column is made by whirling a salt solution around in a centrifuge, thus applying artificially high 'gravity' to it, just as astronauts are trained to withstand high gravity by whirling them round at the end of a long arm; the salt then tends to 'settle out' towards the bottom of the column and produces a slight gradation of density. DNA introduced into the column settles at the point where its density matches that of the salt solution at the same level. Plate 35 shows actual photographs of the centrifuge tubes of Meselson and Stahl, after they had done this experiment. The tubes show that in the original bacteria there is heavy DNA. After one generation of growth in the light medium we have a medium-heavy DNA and after two generations we have a mixture of normal DNA and medium-heavy DNA. In other words, the behaviour of the DNA follows precisely our predictions based on the Watson-Crick replication hypothesis. This experiment was so simple and its interpretation so unambiguous—a classical example of a crucial experiment—that, ever since, biologists have increasingly accepted that the Watson-Crick replication hypothesis must be true, and even though the difficulties about unwinding are still not completely solved there is no doubt at all that this is actually what happens during cell division.

So much, then, for the first function of DNA, the function

of self-replication. We have seen how the Watson-Crick double helix structure makes a beautifully simple prediction about how replication might take place, and we have seen how this prediction has been confirmed by a very simple and decisive experiment. In the next two chapters we shall talk about the two other principal functions of DNA. First, how does it direct protein synthesis—the making of proteins in the cell? That is, how does the hereditary information emerge in the shape of characteristic enzyme and protein molecules in the daughter cells? And, secondly, how is the information actually stored along the DNA strand? In other words, what is the nature of the DNA code?

7

The Messenger of the Genes

In Chapter 6 we described the double helical model of DNA and showed how it explained both the base-pairing rules of Chargaff and the DNA X-ray pattern. We also showed how it led naturally to a delightfully simple scheme for the replication which must take place in going from one generation to the next. We may assume that the hereditary information which is passed from parent to progeny must be contained in the sequence of the DNA bases, A, G, C, and T, because except in respect of these bases the molecule is the same at all points along its length; the main chain simply repeats itself without variation. So we have to suppose that the sequence of bases must form some kind of coded message, and that this message is the hereditary information. The problem of discovering the actual nature of the code will be left over to the next chapter. For the moment, we shall simply assume that some kind of code does in fact exist, and discuss a different problem, namely the mechanism by which the coded information expresses itself, that is to say, the way in which it is used to direct the development of the progeny cell and to confer upon it the properties characteristic of the particular species we are concerned with.

In terms of the one-gene-one-enzyme hypothesis, and knowing that DNA contains a linear sequence of bases, and protein a linear sequence of amino acids, we can rephrase our problem by asking how the chromosomal DNA base sequence

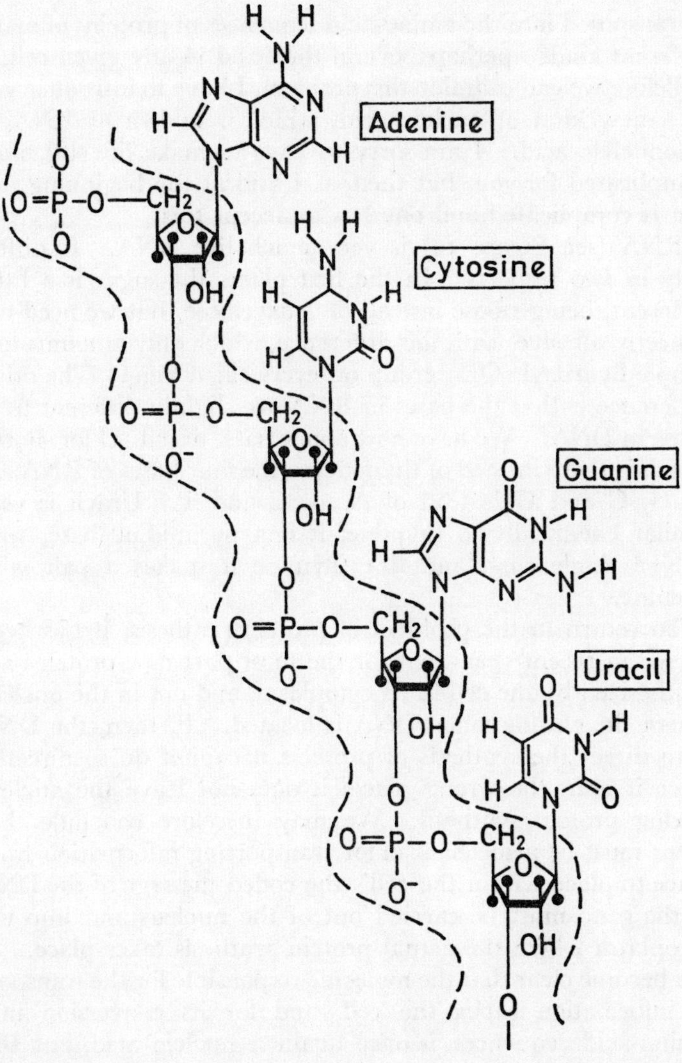

Fig. 12. The formula of ribonucleic acid (RNA). As in DNA, the main chain is extended indefinitely in both directions and the sequence of bases is irregular.

After Watson, J. D. (1965), in Molecular Biology of the Gene, *p. 304. New York: Benjamin, Inc.*

is transposed into the amino-acid sequences of proteins of many different kinds—perhaps several thousand in any given cell.

Before we can examine this problem, I have to introduce you to a new kind of nucleic acid, which is known as RNA or ribonucleic acid. I am sorry to have to make life still more complicated for you, but then, as I said at the beginning, life just is complicated and one has to accept this.

RNA (see Figure 12) is very much like DNA. It differs only in two respects. In the first place, the sugar is a little different, being ribose instead of deoxyribose, but we need not concern ourselves with this difference, which only amounts to a simple hydroxyl (OH) group on every sugar ring. The other difference is that the bases in RNA are slightly different from those in DNA. We have now a new base, uracil (U for short), which is there instead of thymine, so the four bases of RNA are A, G, C and U instead of A, G, C and T. Uracil is very similar chemically to thymine; it is a pyrimidine base, with only a single ring, and like thymine it makes a pair with adenine.

To return to the problem of protein synthesis, it has been shown in recent years that for the most part new proteins are synthesized by the cell in its cytoplasm, and not in the nucleus where the chromosomal DNA is located. If, then, the DNA is to direct the synthesis of proteins it cannot do so directly, since it is in the wrong place: it does not leave the nucleus during protein synthesis. We may therefore conclude that there must be a mechanism for transporting information from place to place within the cell—the coded message of the DNA in the gene must be carried out of the nucleus and into the cytoplasm where the actual protein synthesis takes place. It has become clear that the molecule responsible for the transport of information *within* the cell, and for its conversion into amino-acid sequences, is once again a nucleic acid, but this time it is the new variety we have just met, namely RNA—while, as we have seen, information is transmitted *between* cells by DNA.

There are several sorts of RNA, and in this chapter we are going to meet three of them. These are known as ribosomal RNA, transfer RNA, and messenger RNA.

Let us first take a look at the actual sites of protein synthesis; they are tiny particles called ribosomes (Plate 36), and most living cells are full of them. Mostly they are attached to membranes forming a dense network in the cytoplasm (Plate 37), that is to say outside the nucleus, and it has been known for quite a long time that it is on the ribosomes that protein synthesis actually takes place. They are, as it were, the assembly line of the cell's protein-making factory. One can separate ribosomes completely from a cell, and by giving them proper auxiliary machinery (enzymes) and adequate supplies of raw material and energy, one can actually make them synthesize proteins in a test tube, provided only that they also have access to an information store of the right kind. This so-called 'cell-free system' has been immensely valuable in studies of the way proteins are synthesized.

Ribosomes are made of protein and RNA, and the latter is known as ribosomal RNA. It has to be admitted that at present we simply do not know what this RNA is there for. At one time it was thought that the ribosomal RNA was the actual template on which the protein was assembled; in other words that the code along the ribosomal RNA chain corresponded to the amino-acid sequence of the particular protein made by that ribosome; but we know now that this was too simple an idea. Possibly ribosomal RNA has some kind of structural role; but certainly it now appears that *any* ribosome can make *any* protein given the right information, and that this information comes from outside and is not part of the ribosome itself.

The carrier of the information is one of the other varieties of RNA which we mentioned above, namely messenger RNA, and its function is to pick up information from the place where it is *stored*, that is on the DNA of the chromosomes in the nucleus, and to carry it to the places where it is *used*, the ribosomes out in the cytoplasm. Messenger RNA was discovered quite recently, as the result of a great deal of very clever experimentation, which I wish there was room to describe. In many cells messenger RNA seems to be a very unstable substance. Apparently, as soon as it has done its job of making a few protein molecules, it often falls to pieces. In any case there is not very much of it in the cell at any given time, so it was really very difficult to find it in the first place, though its existence had been predicted once the need for an information carrier within the cell had been appreciated.

The experimental evidence for the sequence of events I am now going to describe is quite complicated, and for the sake of simplicity I shall simply describe to you the remarkable mechanism whose details have been elucidated by all this work, without describing the way in which it was discovered.

The scheme is somewhat as follows (see Figure 13). Inside the nucleus of the cell the messenger RNA is made by base pairing with one strand of the chromosomal DNA. We do not know the details of this process, but it must certainly take place. By the usual base pairing rules, only with U everywhere replacing T as the 'opposite number' of A, we get a strand of messenger RNA the base sequence of which is complementary to one of the strands of the DNA.* A single messenger strand corresponds either to a single protein molecule, or else perhaps to one or two—at any rate a small number. When it has been made, the messenger comes out into the cytoplasm, wanders around until it finds a ribosome, and becomes attached to it.

The next requirement is to bring amino acids up to the ribosomes so that they can become hooked together to form a polypeptide chain. Moreover these amino acids must be brought up *in the correct order*, to correspond to the coded message along the messenger RNA. But we now face a logical difficulty; a string of nucleic acid bases is capable of 'recognizing' other nucleic acid bases (as in DNA replication), but not amino acids. We can easily understand how bases recognize bases (by the usual pairing rules), but there is no obvious chemical mechanism by which a sequence of bases might 'recognize' an amino acid. To get over this impasse the suggestion was made, long before it was proved in practice, that there must be an adaptor molecule, something which, so to speak, at one end of itself could recognize a sequence of a few bases on the messenger RNA chain, and at the other end of itself could specifically hook on to the right amino acid. The prediction was con-

---

* Messenger RNA is single-stranded, unlike the double strands of DNA.

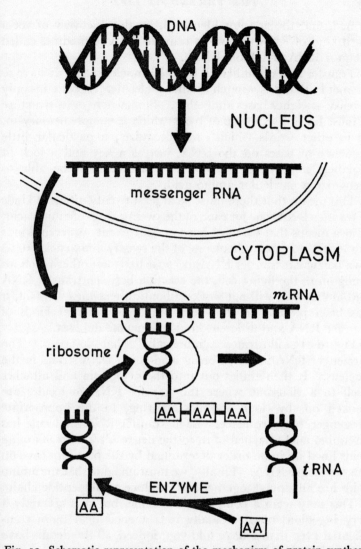

DNA

NUCLEUS

messenger RNA

CYTOPLASM

*m*RNA

ribosome

AA—AA—AA

*t*RNA

ENZYME

AA

AA

Fig. 13. Schematic representation of the mechanism of protein synthesis.
AA = amino acid; *t*RNA = transfer RNA; *m*RNA = messenger RNA.
The ribosome moves along the messenger RNA strand, and as it does so
*t*RNA molecules, each loaded with the appropriate amino acid, are attached
at the ribosome to the *m*RNA strand in turn.   As each *t*RNA is released to
make way for the next, it leaves its amino acid behind to form part of the
growing polypeptide chain.

firmed, and the adaptor identified, by the discovery of yet a third kind of RNA, known as transfer RNA (sometimes called adaptor RNA or soluble RNA).

Transfer RNA is unlike all the other nucleic acids we have so far met in that it is a much smaller molecule. It contains only seventy or eighty bases altogether. Somewhere in its structure it must have a sequence of bases which is complementary to, or in other words which can 'recognize', a particular little sequence of bases on the RNA, just as a key and a lock fit together; some other part of its structure must be able to recognize a particular amino acid.

This means that there must be at least twenty different kinds of transfer RNA, one for each of the twenty kinds of amino acid. It also means that we must have at least twenty different kinds of specific enzyme, to hook one of the twenty amino acids to its own particular transfer RNA, because like most other reactions going on in the living cell, the reaction between transfer RNA and amino acid will not work without an enzyme. In fact, it has been possible to show that all these different kinds of transfer RNA and different kinds of enzyme do exist.

Figure 13 illustrates symbolically what happens. The messenger RNA is shown being made on a DNA strand in the nucleus. It then comes out into the cytoplasm and attaches itself to a ribosome where the transfer RNA molecules are hooked on, by 'lock and key' pairing, to the appropriate messenger base sequence. Each transfer RNA molecule has an amino acid attached to it, so the net result is a set of amino acids lined up in an order determined by the base sequence on the messenger RNA. Finally, we must imagine that the amino acids are all zipped together and produce a polypeptide chain.

This may seem a complicated scheme, but it is certainly a very ingenious one. Actually it is a good deal more complicated even than I have told you; indeed, all the details have not yet been worked out, because this is very recent work and the messenger itself was only discovered as lately as 1960. I will mention just two of the complications.

First of all, the ribosomes themselves are not simple structures. They are built of two sub-units, one large piece and one small piece. We still have only the vaguest of ideas why.

Secondly, it has been found that the ribosomes which are active in protein synthesis seem always to be strung together, in fives and sixes, or even more, on a strand of messenger RNA. These multiple structures, called polysomes, are the ones which really make the protein. The polysomes of different sizes can be separated from the individual ribosomes and it is found that it is they, rather than the separate ribosomes, which are really doing the work.

Plate 38 is an electron microscope picture of polysomes. The fascinating thing is that the ribosomes in this group can actually be seen to be attached together by a very thin thread of material, and there is extremely good evidence that in fact this thread is the messenger RNA itself; so here we can actually see and photograph, in the flesh, as it were, this fantastically thin molecule whose existence in the first place was deduced only indirectly, as a necessary logical consequence of the fact that protein synthesis and chromosomes are located in different parts of the cell. In the polysome it would seem that one messenger is synthesizing a number of proteins simultaneously; a ribosome hooks on at one end of the messenger, and then, as it were, walks along from one end to the other, synthesizing protein as it goes. When it comes to the far end it drops off, as it does so releasing a complete protein molecule (Figure 14).

Now the essence of the whole scheme is that biological information is *one-dimensional*; it is arranged in a linear sequence, like a string of beads. In proteins the polypeptide chain is a linear sequence of amino acids; and we have seen how the information contained in nucleic acids, both in DNA and in the messenger, is also arranged linearly like a line of type in a book. But we have also seen that most proteins are three-dimensional, often nearly spherical, objects in which the polypeptide chains are folded up in a very complicated and specific pattern—look again at the model of myoglobin in Plate 22. We may well ask how the polypeptide chain in myoglobin gets folded up, because so far our scheme allows only for the one-dimensional aspect of the protein, for the sequence of amino acids along its chain. Is the folding process spontaneous, or is there some additional mechanism providing information which determines the way in which the

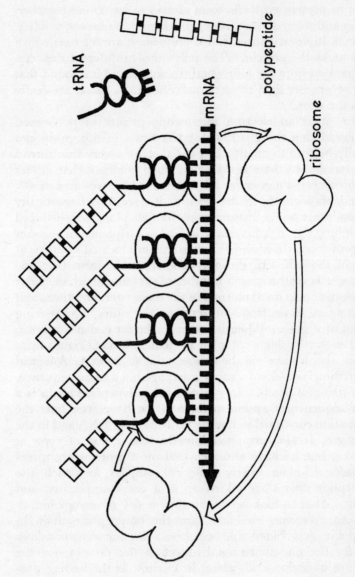

Fig. 14. Protein synthesis on a polysome. Several ribosomes are attached to a single mRNA strand, and each one synthesizes a protein molecule as it moves from one end of the mRNA to the other.

protein folds up after its chain has been synthesized? This would presumably be some kind of three-dimensional template or mould, but there is really no evidence that such a thing exists for any protein in the cell, let alone for the thousands of different proteins each cell contains. Indeed, it is exceedingly hard to see how such a scheme could be made to work—just think of the formidable problems involved in making a three-dimensional mould even for a *model* of a protein (like that illustrated in Plate 23) let alone for the protein itself. It would be impossible ever to get the model out of the mould once it had been formed.

In fact, it is now generally thought, though not absolutely proved, that the protein once synthesized as a linear sequence folds *itself* up, that is to say that it spontaneously assumes the complex arrangement we see. This simple hypothesis has seemed even more plausible since it has quite recently been shown that protein molecules such as enzymes can be unrolled, and then in a test tube, without ribosomes, without nucleic acid—in fact, without any of the apparatus of the living cell—the protein will fold itself up again, in a matter of minutes regaining all its original activity as an enzyme.

That proteins can fold up spontaneously is a further incentive to us to study more of their three-dimensional structures because, if we knew the rules which tell the chain how to fold itself, then presumably, if we could just determine the amino-acid sequence of some new protein we were interested in, we could deduce what its three-dimensional configuration must be, and save all the trouble of doing an X-ray analysis. But this, I think, will take us quite a long time to be able to do.

To recapitulate: we have described a scheme whereby the information in the nuclear DNA is copied on to a strand of RNA, known as the messenger. The messenger moves out into the cytoplasm and there one or more ribosomes attach themselves and move along it, synthesizing protein as they go, the amino acids being brought to this assembly line and ordered in the appropriate sequence by the coding arrangements whereby the transfer RNA attached to each amino acid recognizes its appropriate place on the messenger.

When, in Chapter 5, we first talked about nucleic acid as

the hereditary molecule of every living cell, I pointed out that it could only act in this capacity if it possessed three different attributes—the ability to replicate itself, the ability to carry information, and the ability to direct the synthesis of proteins. We have already discussed the first and third of these, and in the next chapter we shall think about the second, the way in which the sequences of bases along the nucleic acid strand corresponds to a sequence of amino acids in the proteins whose synthesis it directs. This is the so-called coding problem. Remarkably rapid progress has been made very recently, and indeed we now have an almost complete solution of this problem, which might, on the face of it, seem to be one of such extraordinary difficulty that only a few years ago no one would have dreamed that it might be solved in our generation.

8

Mutations and the Code

IN the last two chapters we simply assumed that hereditary information is stored in a DNA or RNA strand in the form of a coded sequence of bases; without concerning ourselves with the details of the code we proceeded to enquire, first of all how the information is passed from nucleus to nucleus when cells divide—which led us to the DNA replication scheme—and, secondly, how information is transported by messenger RNA within a single cell from the chromosomes in the nucleus to the ribosomes in the cytoplasm, where it is used to synthesize specific sequences of amino acids.

In this chapter we shall discuss the nature of the code itself, but first let us think a little about mutations, those sudden alterations in the genetic material which produce consequent changes in the appearance or functioning of the organism. In the light of what we have already learnt, we must now, of course, think of the alterations in the genetic material as changes in the base sequences of the DNA of the nucleus, and of the consequent changes in the organism as being due to changes in the amino-acid sequence of one or more of its proteins. The effects of the genetic alterations are sometimes quite slight but often they are very harmful, as we have seen in the case of abnormal haemoglobins. Often, too, a random mutation may destroy completely the function of the particular protein whose amino-acid sequence has thereby been altered, and the organism will then probably be unable to survive; in such a case

we speak of a lethal mutation.   Occasionally, however, mutations can actually be beneficial, and in this case they may
sometimes, by the process of natural selection, actually become
incorporated into the normal DNA complement of later
generations of the animal or plant.

What kinds of mutation can we envisage?   If we think of
the hereditary information as a particular sequence of bases on
the DNA, it can be compared to a message written in code, and
a mutation would be rather like a misprint in the line of type.
Here are a few examples, taken from newspaper articles, of the
kinds of misprint which are liable to happen:

SAY IT WITH GLOWERS

We might call this sort of error a SUBSTITUTION; an incorrect
letter has been substituted for the correct one.

THE PRIME MINISTER, WHO SPENT THE WEEK-END IN SCOTLAND SHOOTING PEASANTS, . . .

In this example a letter has been left out, so we may call it a
DELETION.

TREASURY CONTROL OF PUBLIC MONKEYS

Here, on the other hand, an extra letter has found its way
into the type; it is an INSERTION.

PUT OUR TRUST IN THE UNTIED NATIONS

Here a section of type has been put in backwards; we may
describe it as an INVERSION.
Finally, a sentence can sometimes suddenly turn into gibberish; this we simply call NONSENSE.

BBC SCIENCE PROGRAMMES ARE FRDOHMRF GPT YJR INOM

In fact, every one of these kinds of misprint is known to occur
in the genetic material of living organisms, and the names I
have given them are the names used by geneticists to describe
the corresponding mutations. We shall be talking about
three of them in this chapter.

How do mutations arise?   It is common knowledge these
days that mutations can be induced by radiation; we are all,
unfortunately, used to the idea that radioactive fall-out from

nuclear weapons produces genetic effects. In fact, many of the natural mutations which occur in living organisms are probably caused by the low-intensity radiation to which we are all exposed every day of our lives whether we like it or not, and quite apart from atomic bomb tests. Some kinds are man-made, like the X-rays used for medical purposes, the radio-active emanations from luminous wristwatches, etc. Other kinds are natural—rocks are radioactive, cosmic rays from outer space are a form of radiation, and there is always a proportion of radioactive substances in our bodies (thus we all contain potassium, and all natural potassium is slightly radioactive).

Then again, mutations can be induced by chemicals. Thus the simple substance known as nitrous acid affects several bases, for example turning cystosine into uracil, thus causing the type of mutation we have called a *substitution*. There is another class of chemical, known as the acridines, which sometimes produces an *insertion* by introducing an additional base into the sequence, and sometimes produces a *deletion* by removing a base.

I have mentioned this topic because the study of natural mutations, and the production of artificial ones by chemicals or by radiation, played a major role in the vast mass of experimental work which lies behind all the discoveries we have been discussing in this book. In particular, mutations have been very important in studying the nature of the genetic code, to which we shall now turn our attention.

We can think of the genetic code as being rather like the Morse code. In the Morse code there are three symbols, dot, dash and space (the space which separates successive letters), whereas in the nucleic acid code we have the four symbols A, G, C and T (A, G, C and U in RNA).

The difficulty of studying the code is simply that we cannot at the moment determine directly the base sequence in nucleic acid in the same sort of way as we can the amino-acid sequence of proteins, described in Chapter 3.* If nucleic acid base

---

* It has recently been announced that Professor Holley and his collaborators have determined the complete sequence of one kind of transfer RNA. This is a tremendous achievement—but it must be remembered that transfer RNA is a relatively small molecule, containing only seventy-seven bases. Genetic DNA is enormously longer, containing up to a million bases or more, and we are still very far from determining the base sequence in such a molecule.

sequences could be worked out, of course all that we should have to do would be to isolate the messenger RNA which goes to produce a particular protein, determine the base sequence of the messenger and the amino-acid sequence of the protein, then finally lay the two sequences alongside one another, and the code would be revealed. But since we cannot do this directly, we have to attack the problem in a roundabout manner.

The first question to be settled is the value of the 'coding ratio'. That is to say, how many symbols are required to specify a single amino acid? In the Morse code, the coding ratio is variable. Some letters of the alphabet are specified by one symbol, for example a single dot means E (coding ratio one); some by two symbols, such as dash, dash, specifying M (coding ratio two); and up to four, for example, dash, dot, dash dash specifying Y (coding ratio four).

In the case of the nucleic acids we know that the coding ratio *must* be more than two, because with four symbols taken in groups of two we can get only $4 \times 4 = 16$ possible combinations. So the coding ratio must be *at least* 3; with four symbols taken three at a time $4 \times 4 \times 4 = 64$ different combinations can be made, which is more than enough to specify 20 different amino acids. This would leave 44 superfluous combinations; what about them? One possibility is that the code might be 'degenerate', as it is called. This is simply a scientist's jargon word, meaning in this case that several *different* combinations of bases might be used for specifying the *same* amino acid, just as two different trade-names might be used to describe the same drug. Or, alternatively, some of those superfluous 44 combinations might simply be nonsense, in other words they might specify nothing, have no meaning. Or, again, the extra combinations might be used like punctuation marks, to indicate the beginning of a new protein, or the end of the last one—it is easy to think of other possibilities. These are alternatives which need to be borne in mind in discussing any code. It must be remembered, however, that they are not mutually exclusive; there could be a code which was degenerate and in which also there were some nonsense combinations.

Until quite a short while ago there was really no experimental evidence with which to test theories about the nature of the code. The coding problem was a wonderful playground for the ingenious puzzle-solver, and indeed also for some very good mathematicians. Several solutions were produced, but none of them could be proved to be correct, although it was quite easy to show that some of them must definitely be wrong.

Just to give a single example of the ingenious codes which were proposed in the past, I will mention Gamow's solution which was one of the first to be proposed seriously. His was a code of overlapping triplets, and it has the very attractive feature that it naturally produced the 'magic number' of 20 combinations (for the 20 amino acids). The sort of scheme he had in mind is illustrated in Figure 15. You will see that in

DNA Sequence A T T **G** C A T C G A C C — — — —

A T T	symbol for first amino acid
T T **G**	symbol for second amino acid
T **G** C	symbol for third amino acid
G C A	symbol for fourth amino acid
C A T	symbol for fifth amino acid
— — —	etc.

Fig. 15. Gamow's proposal for a genetic code of overlapping triplets. The first amino acid would be coded by the first, second and third bases; the second amino acid by the second, third and fourth bases, and so on.

This scheme gives 20 independent combinations, corresponding to the 20 amino acids.

A change in a single base, for example the **G** in heavy type, would alter three successive amino acids—the second, third and fourth in this example.

A code of this kind imposes restrictions on possible amino-acid sequences. For example, the amino acid coded by A T T could only be followed by an amino acid whose code symbol began with T T. Non-overlapping codes are not restricted in this way.

After Crick, F. H. C., Scientific American, *October, No. 10, p. 66* (1962).

this code each base forms part of the symbol for three neighbouring amino acids. But it was quite easy to show that this scheme could not be right, partly because, as you will see if you think about it a little while, a code of this kind would impose restrictions on the possible sequences of amino acids in protein. If it was right, certain amino-acid sequences could never occur, but in fact it was found that these restrictions did not actually apply. Again a point mutation, that is to say a substitution of a *single* base, would change *three* neighbouring amino acids, and never less than three. But we know that in fact this is not what happens; we have already mentioned the example of the abnormal haemoglobins, in which only a single amino acid is changed, and in general amino-acid abnormalities are nearly always found singly and not in threes. So Gamow's code could not be the correct solution.

A number of other codes were proposed. But only quite recently has real experimental evidence been available, first, as to the general nature of the code and, secondly, as to the actual code combination corresponding to each particular amino acid. I am going to describe two kinds of experiment from which the evidence has come, the first giving information about the general type of code, and the second about the actual symbols and their meanings.

The first set of experiments, about the nature of the code, is easier to understand if I tell you in advance what the right answer is. This is that the code consists of triplets of bases, non-overlapping, and read from a single point, in a specific direction. Thus the sequence, AGCTTCCGT . . . would be read AGC, TTC, CGT . . . and so on until you get to the end of the gene; each triplet would specify a particular amino acid (actually serine, phenylalanine, arginine . . .). This result was obtained by studying certain mutants of microorganisms produced by acridine. You will remember that acridine treatment has the effect either of inserting an additional base into the sequence, or of deleting a base; sometimes it does one and sometimes the other.

We can most easily see how the experiments went by using our Morse code analogy. Consider the word WOODWORK, in Morse code, as the beginning of a message:

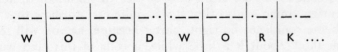

(In order to make the analogy as close as possible to the DNA code, I have chosen a word composed only of letters which have three symbols in Morse code, and I have left out the spaces.)

Now if we make an insertion somewhere at random in the middle of this sequence of symbols, if for example a dot is put in after the sixth place, and then we read off the symbols three at a time:

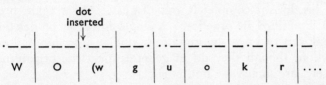

we find that after the point at which the insertion was made the symbols go out of step and the message becomes nonsense. The insertion has produced a string of gibberish, and the nonsense will obviously continue indefinitely for as long as the message goes on. Again, if we make a deletion, it is easy to see that after the point at which the deletion was made we shall again get a string of nonsense. Similarly in a DNA sequence either a single insertion or a single deletion would make the genetic message, and hence the amino-acid sequence of the corresponding protein, go 'haywire' after a certain point; we could predict that the protein produced by a DNA strand treated in this way would become functionless and, if it was an essential one, that the organism would die—the mutation would be lethal. The prediction is borne out in practice; single insertions or deletions are lethal mutations.

But now suppose we introduce an insertion at one point, and then a little later on we make a deletion. Then the message goes out of step at the insertion, turning into nonsense as before; but after the deletion it comes back into step again and the message returns to sense:

If we imagine the DNA treated in the same way, then we see that in the eventual protein there would be just two or three incorrect amino acids, or at any rate a small number (depending on how far the deletion was from the insertion), and after that everything would be normal again, and the amino-acid sequence would once more be correct, so that while the whole protein might not work very well, because it would contain two or three abnormal amino acids, at least it would perhaps not be thrown completely out of gear.   Once again prediction is verified in practice.   A single insertion or deletion is lethal; but two near-by mutations, one an insertion and one a deletion, though they do in general affect the organism adversely, are sometimes not lethal.

The really crucial experiment came when it was possible to put into the same section of DNA three insertions, all close to one another.   As we have just seen, *one* insertion gives us nonsense after the point at which the insertion is located.   It can similarly be shown that a *second* insertion close to the first produces the same result, in other words the message becomes nonsense after the first insertion, but (unlike the case of an insertion followed by a deletion) its meaning is not restored by the second:

But if we put in *three* insertions, we eventually come back to sense because the symbols get back into step again:

This was shown actually to happen in the living organism. *One* insertion is lethal; *two* insertions are lethal; but *three* insertions are non-lethal, even if they have some adverse effect by substituting a short stretch of nonsense in some protein or other.

You will see that this result shows quite clearly that the coding ratio is three; each amino acid is specified by three symbols. If the ratio were four we would have to put in *four* insertions before the message returned once more to sense. This was the experiment which proved almost conclusively that the code must be a triplet code, that it is non-overlapping, and that it is read in threes, from a certain point which we may think of as the beginning of the 'sentence'.

Let us now turn to a second set of experiments, designed to tell us what the actual code combinations are. For this we make use of the so-called cell-free system (see p. 71) in which all the essential components of the protein synthesis mechanism are assembled together in a test tube. The mixture contains ribosomes, a source of energy, a supply of amino acids, some transfer RNA, and a whole series of enzymes. If now some messenger RNA is put into the test tube, the mixture will proceed to manufacture protein. For example, you can put in the messenger for haemoglobin, and the system will produce recognizable haemoglobin molecules.

As we have already indicated, the cell-free system has been extremely valuable for studies of protein synthesis; it can also be used for studying the code. For it was shown that the cell-free system still works if you put in an *artificial* messenger, a piece of synthetic RNA of known base sequence. In the first experiment ever done along these lines the messenger was a synthetic RNA in which every base was uracil, so that the 'message' was simply UUUUU . . .; it was found to cause the system to produce a polypeptide called polyphenylalanine, that is to say a peptide chain in which every amino acid is phenylalanine. It follows, therefore, since we know we have a triplet code, that the code symbol UUU must specify the amino acid phenylalanine:

$$UUUUUU \ldots \rightarrow Phe.Phe. \ldots$$

UUU was the first code symbol to be deciphered. This initial success has stimulated a vast amount of experimental work using other artificial messengers and identifying the polypeptides they produce.

The work has not been easy, partly because the cell-free system is very complicated and no one understands fully how it works (indeed it sometimes refuses to work at all) and partly because it is technically very hard to make artificial RNAs with exactly the sequences of bases you want. This is simply a problem in chemistry, but nevertheless it is quite hard to tackle. In spite of these difficulties it is now possible to list the meanings of nearly all the sixty-four triplet combinations in a kind of base/amino acid code dictionary (Table 1).

Note that the code is degenerate, in the sense we used the word on p. 82—several different code combinations often produce the same amino acid. It is now clear, too, that the code contains one or two triplets which are like punctuation marks; they indicate where the message specifying one protein ends, and the next begins. There may also be some nonsense combinations—symbols without meaning.

Code combinations which are still doubtful have been placed in brackets. One or both of the combinations UAA and UAG may be used as full stops—as signals to terminate an amino-acid chain. Three other combinations are still unaccounted for, but they will probably have been decoded by the time this table is in print.

The code symbols established by working with the cell-free system and artificial messengers can be tested in a quite independent manner. As an example of the kind of test which can be applied, let us consider the abnormal haemoglobins, and specifically sickle-cell haemoglobin. You will remember that in this haemoglobin a particular amino acid (valine) has been substituted for the amino acid normally present at that place in the chain (glutamic acid). Now it happens that another quite different West African blood disease has been found to be due to substitution of the same glutamic acid, but this time by lysine. It is most likely that these abnormalities are produced by the mutation of a single base in the chromosomal DNA. If this is so, and if the code dictionary is correct, it should be possible to allocate code symbols such that the changes valine

glutamic acid ⟨

lysine

can be explained on the basis of changes in a single base. Reference to the table will show that we can indeed do this, by choosing the symbols

GUG

GAG ⟨

AAG

A great number of abnormalities of quite a few different proteins is now known, so that many tests of this kind can be made. In nearly every case the tests are consistent with the code dictionary in Table 1, a result which could not be due to

TABLE I

The Genetic Code

Phenylalanine	UUU, UUC
Leucine	CUC, (UUG), (CUU), (CUG)
Serine	UCU, UCC, UCA, UCG, AGU, AGC
Tyrosine	UAU, UAC
Cysteine	UGU, UGC
Tryptophan	UGG
Proline	CCU, CCC, CCA, CCG
Histidine	CAU, CAC
Glutamine	CAA, CAG
Arginine	CGU, CGC, CGA, CGG, AGA, AGG
Isoleucine	AUU, AUC, (AUA)
Methionine	AUG
Threonine	ACU, ACC, ACA, ACG
Asparagine	AUU, AAC
Lysine	AAA, AAG
Valine	GUU, GUC, GUA, GUG
Alanine	GCU, GCC, GCA, GCG
Aspartic acid	GAU, GAC
Glutamic acid	GAA, GAG
Glycine	GGU, GGC, GGA, GGG

chance. There is no doubt that the dictionary must be almost completely correct; and although there remain one or two ambiguities, and some difficulties about the few symbols which apparently have no meaning, I am sure that all these will be cleared up very soon.

So we have shown how artificial mutations have been used to establish the nature of the code—that it consists of triplets of bases—and how the cell-free system has been exploited to give us a knowledge of the code symbols themselves, a knowledge which is still not quite complete, but which nevertheless represents one of the triumphs of molecular biology today. Only a few years ago it would indeed have taken a bold man to suggest that a table like this could be drawn up within the present decade.

The next chapter will be concerned with another experimental system which has proved enormously important in molecular biology, namely the viruses. The viruses are important not only because they are used as a powerful experimental tool, but also because they have their own intrinsic interest as examples of biological organization. And of course they are also extremely interesting to us as human beings, because of their function as carriers of disease.

9

Living Architecture—The Viruses

In this chapter we shall be considering one of the smallest forms of life, so small indeed that it possesses only a part of the normal attributes of living organisms. It cannot eat, nor can it grow, and it reproduces only inside the cells of some host organism; it is in the true sense a parasite. I am referring to the viruses. Because they are deficient in so many functions normally attributed to living organisms, and because they often display characteristics which we think of as typical of non-living things—for example, sometimes they form crystals —there have been many arguments in the past whether viruses should be called living or non-living. These arguments are only important if one supposes that there is a fundamental distinction between living things and non-living things, some kind of boundary on one side or the other of which everything must be placed. Personally I do not think there is any evidence of such a boundary, of any difference in essence between the living and the non-living, and I think most molecular biologists would share this view. If it is correct, then the question simply becomes one of convenience, or at the most of semantics and definition, rather than of principle, and in this sense it is perhaps not so interesting.

But whether they are alive or dead, viruses are certainly very important to us because they are agents of disease. Many

of the diseases of man which are still intractable are caused
by viruses. Viruses are hard to deal with because they lack
so many of the normal functions of living things, so the number
of points at which they are open to attack is very limited.
For example, they lack a metabolic apparatus—they have no
chemical factory of their own, and instead make use of that
belonging to their host; an attack in this quarter would do as
much harm to the host as to the virus.

Viruses attack not only human beings, but also other
animals, plants, and even bacteria. They are classified
according to their hosts, as animal viruses, plant viruses, and
bacteriophages, the bacteriophages being viruses which attack
bacteria. Viruses eluded detection for a long time because
they are exceedingly small objects. They generally cannot
be seen in an ordinary microscope. They pass through even
very fine filters, hence their old name, the 'filtrable viruses'.

But they can be seen in the electron microscope. Plates 39
onward show some pictures of them. Though they are so
very small they are large compared with many of the objects
we have been talking about hitherto—perhaps a thousand
times bigger than an ordinary protein molecule.

Viruses are important not only in their own right, but also
in biology generally; they are wonderful tools for research.
The reason for this is that, lacking as they do the power of
growth or any metabolic apparatus, they can be thought of as
organisms purely concerned with reproduction. In them the
functions of reproduction and heredity can be studied in isola-
tion, as it were; for the geneticist they are ideal experimental
material. Furthermore, they reproduce themselves so rapidly
that if you wish to study genetical changes and the appearance
of mutations, you have to wait a much shorter time than with
other organisms.

Viruses are made of protein and nucleic acid, and the nucleic
acid may be either DNA or RNA. You will not be surprised
after reading the last few chapters to hear that in the viruses
too it is the nucleic acid which carries the hereditary information. The protein seems to be simply a protective coat, designed
to protect the nucleic acid against its external environment. We
shall have more to say about this protective coat later on.

When a virus makes its attack, somehow or other its nucleic acid finds its way into the host cell, and often only a few minutes later the cell bursts open and releases about a hundred or more new virus particles all ready to find new hosts.

It is an extraordinary process—a sort of cellular take-over—for one finds that the host cell's normal apparatus has been abruptly closed down—its DNA disintegrates, and makes no more messenger RNA, the virus nucleic acid assumes control and produces its own messenger RNA. The host's protein synthesis mechanism is compelled to manufacture the enzymes and coat protein molecules needed for the production of virus components and their assembly. New virus particles begin to appear inside the host cell until finally it bursts and releases them. Many stages of this astonishing process, whereby the host cell is forced to subject itself to the purposes of the virus like a ship taken over by a crew of pirates, can be seen directly in the electron microscope as well as studied chemically.

It is quite a difficult problem to discover how to interfere with this process, how to stop the virus multiplication without also interfering with normal, uninfected cells, since the virus is actually making use of normal cell processes. It is only very recently that there has come a real hope of truly selective action against the virus, in the discovery of interferon, a substance synthesized by cells which seems to have the special function of attacking foreign nucleic acids such as virus nucleic acid. We must hope that interferon can be mobilized as a practical weapon against virus diseases.

Many of the discoveries mentioned earlier in this book have been made by working with viruses. They are ideal experimental material for all kinds of studies of heredity, of mutation, of protein synthesis, and of DNA replication. But viruses are also of great interest as objects in their own right, as pieces of molecular architecture. They come in all sorts of fascinating shapes, which raise many interesting questions—why do they have these shapes? How did they originate, and what is their purpose? How are they assembled? We shall now look at a few examples of virus architecture.

Let us begin with a bacteriophage, the kind of virus which attacks bacteria. Plate 40 shows models of one of these strange organisms, and with them are photographs of the actual bacteriophage itself. You can see it has a head and a tail (Plate 40a, b). The head is made of protein and inside it is a tremendously long string of nucleic acid—DNA in most cases (see Plate 41). The head is hexagonal in cross section and attached to it is a long tubular tail and a kind of helical spring wound round it. There are also so-called tail fibres attached to a base plate at the end of the spring. When the bacteriophage attacks (Plate 40c, d), it sits down tail first on a bacterium and the tail fibres stick it to the surface; the spring is released and as it contracts it pushes the tail—like a hypodermic needle—into the cell and after that the DNA is injected through the tail tube into the cell, and there gets on with its work. You can see pictures of this process, at various stages, in Plates 42 and 43.

It is really an incredible arrangement. And, actually, more is probably known about the details of the working and behaviour of this tiny object than of any other living organism at all, and not only about the mechanics of its extraordinary injection apparatus. Its chromosome, its DNA strand, has been mapped to a remarkably fine degree of detail, so that in some regions of it one can even deduce the actual order of some of the DNA bases. Its messenger RNA, that is to say the messenger RNA whose synthesis it induces once it gets into its host cell, was in fact the first messenger ever to be discovered. Bacteriophage was also used in the experiments from which it was possible to deduce that the DNA code was a triplet, as I described in the last chapter.

Let us now look at the quite different kind of virus shown in Plate 44. This is an example of a so-called rod-shaped virus, and this time it is a virus which attacks plant cells. It is called tobacco mosaic virus, from a well-known disease which it produces in the tobacco plant. It forms long rods, and in the best electron microscope pictures it can be seen that each rod has a hole down its axis. Close observation shows that the rod is not continuous. It is apparently made up of small sub-units, rather like a pine cone.

Strangely enough, though tobacco mosaic virus is a very large object compared with the protein molecules we have

considered earlier in the book, it was in fact the earliest biological object to be studied with some success by X-ray methods.
It gives a beautiful X-ray picture, Plate 45, which contains
hundreds of reflections; even thirty years ago it was possible to
deduce from a picture like this that tobacco mosaic virus was
built of a large number of sub-units.   By studying electron
microscope pictures and X-ray photographs it has now been
possible to arrive at a very detailed model of its structure (Plate
46). Basically it is a helix—rather like the helices we have met
before, for example in DNA and in the alpha helix of the
polypeptide chain.   But it is a helix on an enormously larger
scale, for a single virus particle contains over 2000 sub-units,
and each of these sub-units is a protein molecule just about as
big as the myoglobin molecule.   So we have a particle made up
of over 2000 sub-units each containing some 2500 atoms—in all
something like five million atoms.   Our model also contains a
helical wire, spiralling along inside the sub-units—this is the
virus nucleic acid (RNA this time), a single long strand which
enters a cell of the tobacco leaf and there reproduces its kind.

Tobacco mosaic virus, though large, has a particularly simple
construction and consists as far as we know of only two components, of an RNA strand and of protein sub-units all of
which are identical with one another.   This simplicity has
made it very important in studies of the nucleic acid code. We
can very easily obtain a preparation of virus protein by causing
the rod to disintegrate; and because all the protein sub-units
are identical, we do not need to separate them further before
making chemical studies, for example determining their amino-
acid sequence—and in fact the complete sequence of tobacco
mosaic virus protein has now been worked out.   If we induce
mutations in the nucleic acid, by exposing it to radiation or to
suitable chemicals (the so-called mutagens like nitrous acid or
acridine)—if, in other words, we artificially make changes in
the RNA base sequence—the protein sub-units will change their
sequence in the next generation in sympathy, and by noting
what types of amino-acid changes occur we can check up on our
code dictionary just as we did with abnormal haemoglobins.

Finally, let us look at a third kind of virus, the class of so-
called spherical viruses (Plate 39).   Some well-known animal

viruses are of this kind, the virus responsible for poliomyelitis for example. At first sight in the electron microscope, viruses of this type look as if they were tiny spheres—hence the name —but on closer examination it is apparent that they are always made of small sub-units.

Sometimes 'spherical' viruses even have flat faces. For example, Plate 47 shows some pictures of a virus which attacks insects, called *Tipula* Iridescent virus. Each particle in these pictures casts a shadow, and this is made by spraying the preparation of virus with a fine jet of metal atoms from a particular direction before the pictures are taken. In this picture the particles have been double shadowed, by spraying successively from two different directions. You can see that the shadows have sharp angles, showing that the particles cannot be round like spheres but must have flat faces and sharp edges like polyhedra. Their precise form was established by comparing these shadows with the shadows thrown by various types of polyhedra, and it was shown that the only polyhedral model which would reproduce the observed shapes of shadow was an icosahedron—a regular solid with twenty triangular faces (Plate 48).

In my first chapter I referred to the surprise of finding geometrical order in biological systems. And here, perhaps, is the most extraordinary case of all. The icosahedron is one of the so-called Platonic solids (Figure 16), one of the five regular solids first discovered by the early Greek philosophers, and ever since a plaything for mathematicians, but not perhaps of much practical consequence. It is remarkable that these rather esoteric objects should have become a subject of furious controversy among biologists trying to decide the exact shapes of minute agents of disease. It now seems that in fact all the 'spherical' viruses are basically icosahedra, or modified forms thereof.

Plate 49 shows another example. It is the adenovirus, responsible for some of the respiratory infections of man, and in this picture we can actually see the sub-units making up the flat triangular faces. (The model in Plate 50, made of ping-pong balls, will be useful for comparison.) You can count six particles along each edge, and the whole surface is made up of

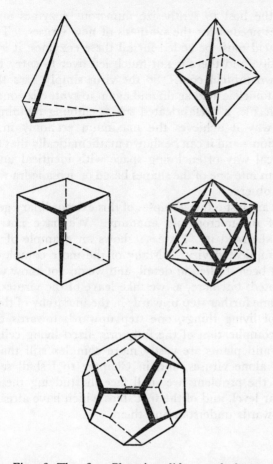

Fig. 16. The five Platonic solids: tetrahedron,
octahedron, cube, icosahedron and dodecahed-
ron.

precisely 252 particles. Somewhere tucked away inside is the
nucleic acid, but we do not yet know how this is arranged, so
the viruses still have some secrets to yield up.

One might ask—why a regular solid? And, more specifically, why an icosahedron? It seems to be a question of
economy—economy of genetic information. The virus particle has to take over the metabolism of its host cell—it must

G

compel the host to synthesize numerous enzymes and other molecules needed for the synthesis of new viruses. The virus nucleic acid must be coded for all these enzymes; it is limited in quantity, and there is not much left over to carry the code for its own protein coat. So the virus simply uses the same section of nucleic acid again and again to synthesize one type of coat molecule, a prefabricated self-assembling building block. In this way it achieves the maximum economy in genetic information—and it can be shown mathematically that the most economical way of enclosing space with identical units is to form them into one of the shapes based on icosahedra which we actually observe.

Those are just a few glimpses of this extraordinary geometric world of sub-microscopic anatomy. We have not by any means exhausted it. Plate 51 shows an example of an even more complicated virus. Many of the more complex shapes have not been studied in detail, and we do not know why they are adopted; but here, as we take leave of the viruses, we are making one further step upwards in the hierarchy of the organization of living things, one step upwards towards the even greater complication of the fully organized living cell. Most animals and plants are vastly more complex still than single cells, let alone viruses, and in Chapter 10 I shall say something of the problems we shall face in studying these at the molecular level, and of the first steps which have already been taken towards understanding them.

10

The Way Ahead

THIS book has been concerned with one particular approach to biology—an approach which has been highly profitable in the last few years, and which is beginning to illuminate more clearly wide areas of the field. But I do not want to leave you with the idea that molecular biology is the whole of biology. Biology, the study of the world of living things, is a vast subject. It is studied from many points of view by people with very different interests using very different techniques and skills. It includes systematic biology, ecology, physiology, psychology, biochemistry, and many other disciplines. All these approaches have their own validity, and all of them can make and, at different stages in the development of the subject, have made dramatic contributions to it. So when I write of molecular biology, I do not wish to convey the impression that this is nowadays the only part of the field which is successful or interesting. It certainly is not. Rather it is one particular approach to biology which happens to have achieved dramatic successes during the past ten years or more, and which seems likely to go on doing so for quite a time to come.

What I have tried to do is to give the simplest possible picture of a very complex field of research. I have simplified it because only so was I able to give a compact bird's eye view of this area of biology. But it is not only I who have simplified. Molecular biologists, as part of their working approach, have had to simplify biology also, because only in this way could they hope to produce a coherent picture out of the enormous complexities of living organisms.

I referred earlier to the resemblance between different kinds of living cell, and to the concept of the generalized cell with its standard apparatus including the nucleus, the cytoplasm, ribosomes, the messenger, and so on, and having standard metabolic machinery.   This implies that identical sequences of chemical reactions occur in different kinds of cell from different animals.   The genetic code, too, is probably standardized; there is pretty good evidence by now that to a large extent at least the code is common to different animals and plants.   The very same base combinations are used to code a particular amino acid over a very wide range of living things.   This has been shown, for example, by using the 'cell-free' system described above (page 71).   You can take the cell-free system from one kind of animal (A) and add to it messenger RNA derived from a second animal (B).   You then find that the system synthesizes new protein which is characteristic of animal B and not of animal A.   In other words the protein synthetic apparatus of animal A can read the same language as animal B.   This kind of experiment strongly suggests, though it does not finally prove, that the code may indeed be a universal one.

But in spite of all these resemblances, some of them very fundamental ones, between one cell and another, we know that as a matter of fact cells in many respects differ widely, not only from one organism to another, but also within the same organism.   Thus we know that in a human being there are brain cells, nerve cells, muscle cells, liver cells, red blood cells, all performing extremely different functions, looking and behaving very differently.   And yet all these kinds of cells start from a single fertilized egg by successive division—the egg divides first into two, then into four, then into eight, and so on.   Eventually, differences between one cell and another must appear.

How does it actually happen?   In this remarkable process, known as differentiation, beginning from a single egg we get gradual divergence and specialization into cells performing different functions in the same animal.   Yet we know from studies of the mechanism of mitosis, or cell division, that all the cells in the organism have the same information in them, the same DNA strands. Though the information is the same, the cells turn out to be different in all sorts of ways. They contain, for example, different proteins. Consider the case of haemoglobin. Every cell in the human body has a stretch of DNA in its chromosomes carrying the code for the haemoglobin molecule, and yet haemoglobin is synthesized only in one kind of cell, in the red blood cell. No other kind of human cell contains any haemoglobin at all. It follows that there must be some kind of switch; something which turns off and on particular genes in appropriate circumstances—in this case the gene responsible for haemoglobin—some sort of control system.

We are just at the point of beginning to understand in a few cases how control systems may work. Figure 17 shows a scheme which seems to fit the facts in a number of cases which have recently been worked out.

Let us think of one of the reaction chains in a cell, each step in the sequence being controlled by an enzyme—like the sugar-alcohol chain of reactions in yeast, which I mentioned earlier.

It has been found that often the genes controlling the production of all the enzymes concerned with a particular reaction chain are adjacent on the DNA strand. The set of genes involved in a particular metabolic pathway are grouped together, making up a unit on the chromosome known as an *operon*. It is in some real sense a unit, because it is found that the whole group of genes acts in concert. Either *all* the genes of the group are active, or they are *all* inactive—either all the enzymes are synthesized or none of them. The whole group is switched on or off as a unit. Geneticists have found that the switch mechanism, which is called the *operator*, is situated at one end of the operon—at one end of the group of genes.

Now, how does the switch work? It seems that the operator is switched on unless it is masked by combination with a certain small molecule known as the repressor. If a repressor molecule is attached to the operator the whole group of genes is switched *off*. If repressor is not there the whole group of genes is switched *on*, and produces messengers which migrate out into the cytoplasm and induce the synthesis of the set of enzymes.

Next, where does the repressor come from? It seems to be produced by another quite distinct gene, called the regulator gene, elsewhere in the chromosome; conceivably it might even be in a different chromosome. This regulator gene is responsible for producing repressor molecules which then migrate to the operator and actuate the switch mechanism.

But where does the control come in? In the example shown in Figure 17, the control is exercised by the final product D of the reaction chain A→B→C→D. This product has the property of reacting with the repressor molecule; and the repressor can *only* act if it has first combined with D. If the cell is producing too much of the product D, then the excess of D reacts with the repressor which is then, and only then, able to attach itself to the operator gene and switch off the whole operon, and so indirectly shut down the production of new enzyme molecules. It is a delightfully ingenious automatic control system such as might be used in an automated factory; the production line (the chain of reactions) is only expanded by the formation of new machine tools (enzymes) so long as the final product is in short supply. As soon as adequate supplies of product are coming forward, machine tools are no longer synthesized.

The details of this scheme do not matter too much. Indeed, it has only recently been formulated, and we may not have got the details quite right. Other types of scheme certainly operate in other circumstances. But the general principle evidently has immense possibilities for the control of the complicated and enormous genetic material in a cell.

The need for control is easier to understand if we think in terms of an analogy. We have already used the Morse code, and its equivalence to the alphabet, as an analogy for the working of the genetic code. The analogy between alphabets and genetic information can be developed further. We have called DNA the Thread of Life, but now let us think of it instead as the Book of Life. Think of an amino acid, or its equivalent triplet of bases, as a word. Then a protein molecule, containing a few hundred amino acids, would be roughly equivalent to a paragraph in the book. And we can think of

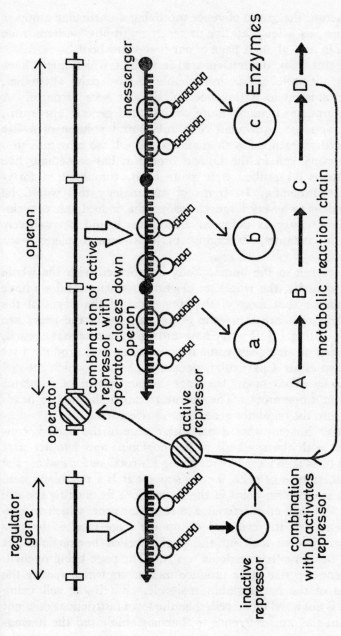

Fig. 17. Schematic representation of one possible mechanism for the genetic control of enzyme synthesis in bacterial cells, proposed by Jacob and Monod. *After Jacob, F., & Monod, J.* J. Mol. Biol., 3, 318 (1961).

an operon, the group of genes specifying a particular group of enzymes, as a few, say five or ten, paragraphs, perhaps 1000 words in all—about a page of our imaginary book.

On this basis, the nucleic acid in a virus, which might have about a couple of hundred thousand base pairs altogether, would amount to a thin book of sixty or seventy pages. A bacterium has a much more complicated genetic apparatus, and might be equivalent to a substantial volume of a few hundred or even a few thousand pages. If we now turn to a man, every cell in the human organism has something like two thousand million base pairs in it, contained in forty-six chromosomes. In terms of an analogy this would be equivalent to a very large encyclopaedia indeed, an encyclopaedia of forty-six volumes. And they would be positively gigantic volumes, averaging perhaps 20,000 pages each (Figure 18).

Every cell in the human body is provided with the whole encyclopaedia, the whole set of chromosomes. And we have to imagine that most of the time most of the pages of the encyclopaedia are shut—the great majority of the genes are not operating. Just every now and again one page is opened, the genes on that page come into operation and produce a set of enzymes for a particular metabolic pathway which the cell requires. What opens the pages is our system of regulator genes and operators. The operators can be likened to headlines, and the regulator genes to cross references.

Let us imagine that a particular page of the book is concerned with the synthesis of haemoglobin, and another part of the book is concerned with giving instructions for making the particular type of cell. Let us suppose it is a red blood cell. Then at a certain point in the instructions for making the cell there will be a cross-reference, a regulator gene, which will, so to speak, tell the cell to look up the page labelled haemoglobin. So we look up the page labelled haemoglobin; it has a headline 'haemoglobin' on it. The page being opened, the genes on that page produce messengers which specify the chains of the haemoglobin molecule. But if the cell being made is not a red blood cell, then the set of instructions does not contain the cross-reference to 'haemoglobin', and the haemo-

Fig. 18.

globin page is therefore never referred to—the haemoglobin genes never become active.

The details of this scheme are quite hypothetical. Indeed, a regulator gene for haemoglobin molecules has not been discovered, but it seems clear that in a general way this is the kind of process which must take place. Actually, we can even *see* the pages of the book opening. Under the microscope, at various stages in the cell's development, certain parts of the chromosome can be seen to swell up (Plate 52). At other stages of development, different parts of the same chromosome become swollen. It is at those swellings that the messenger RNA is being synthesized, and it looks as though the swellings are the equivalent in real life to the opening of the pages of the immense encyclopaedia which we have described in our analogy.

Why does a human cell need a huge encyclopaedia of instructions while a bacterium can get along with one volume?— after all, in a single human cell at any one time the number of different kinds of protein molecule, a few thousand probably, is not greater than the number in an individual bacterial cell, so the number of pages of the human encyclopaedia which are open in any given cell at any given time need be no greater than in the bacterium. But man needs a far bigger encyclopaedia than does a bacterium, because man is a much more complicated organism containing many kinds of cell and exhibiting a much greater complexity of behaviour. The human encyclopaedia is not used, on average, much more often than the bacterial book, perhaps—but it contains far more reference material tucked away, to be ready for any new situation which may arise.

What about mutations? In terms of our analogy mutations are evidently misprints, misprints made in producing new editions of the book of life. Just as in a real book misprints are more likely to produce nonsense than better sense, so mutations will almost always be deleterious, almost always, in fact, they will kill the organism or the cell, often at so early a stage in its existence that we do not even realize it ever came into being at all. Just the very fact that a mutation is lethal may often eliminate the misprint from subsequent editions because the cell containing the misprint can never produce its own kind. In other cases the mutation might be deleterious but not lethal. It would then find its way into new editions, but these deleterious mutations may, one hopes, over generations, be eliminated by the process of natural selection. Just occasionally a mutation might actually be advantageous. It would not be eliminated because it would make the organism better qualified for the struggle of life. Ultimately, such a mutation might be incorporated permanently into the books of life of that species. Such is the process of evolution.

It may seem surprising that a random process like this can improve a species, or even produce a new species, indeed lead eventually to the whole vast diversity of animal and plant life we see around us. But it must be remembered that these processes have operated over an enormous span of time, more than five hundred million years.

So you see that our simple picture of a DNA strand in the chromosome, directing the synthesis of the protein in the cell, is correct as far as it goes, but it is an over-simplification, indeed a gross over-simplification. Living cells are so complicated that we cannot expect any simple scheme like this to be more than a shadow of reality. But as I said at the beginning of the chapter, over-simplification was in the past a necessary condition for progress. Today the situation is changing.

My colleague, Francis Crick, recently wrote that in molecular biology the determination of the structure of DNA was the end of the beginning, and that the elucidation of the code was the beginning of the end. What he meant by the DNA structure being the end of the beginning was, I think, that here for the first time we knew definitely on the molecular scale what one of the essential giant molecules of living cells looked like and what its structure was, so it became possible for the first time to relate a biological function to a molecular structure. What he meant by the second part of his remark, that the elucidation of the code is the beginning of the end, was that the era of simplification is now over. We have probably learned nearly as much as we can by making the tacit assumption that any one cell is very much like any other cell. Now we have to take into account and understand the complications and differences between one sort of cell and another.

There is another way of looking at this. The old biologists on the whole worked from the top down. They started with the whole organism; then they pulled it to pieces and looked at individual organs and tissues; then they examined single cells under the microscope—they were always working downwards from the complicated to the simple. The new biology works from the other end. It works from the bottom up. It started with the simplest aspects of living organisms, with the individual molecules in the cell and their interactions, and it neglected the complications. Now it is necessary to face the complications, to work upwards in the hierarchy of biological organization.

The fact is that life is enormously complicated. In its very essence it involves the replication and maintenance of complex molecular patterns in a hostile environment. It is no accident, I think, that all the way through we have been concerned with giant molecules, the proteins and the nucleic acids. Complex molecules are of the absolute essence of life, because life involves the transmission and preservation of information—and the storage of information demands complexity. So, faced with these complications, we are really only at the beginning of our understanding.

Any scientist, I think, has a set of private pipe dreams of what he hopes his subject will achieve in the future. It is easy to think of a few examples which would probably be in every biologist's list. First of all, we would like to know how to control mutations, how to do away, perhaps, with the bad mutations—and, as I have said before, nearly all mutations are bad—while at the same time encouraging good ones. We can see enough now about the way in which genetic information is carried—that it depends on this sequence of the bases in the DNA and that the mutations which occur are simply random events—to understand that to control them is a matter of enormous technical difficulty. In principle it should be possible to control them, but this is a case where principle and practice are very far apart indeed. And, of course, as many people have pointed out, even if the technical difficulties were solved, the social consequences of being able to exert direct control on human heredity seem too terrifying to think about—

but in my opinion it is extremely important to try to think about them nevertheless.

Then also, we would all like to understand the phenomenon of mind. The study of the central nervous system is a part of biology which is still in a very primitive state. It is, I think, clearly going to be one of the major problems of the future. At the moment we do not even know with any certainty how memory is stored in the brain. Quite a good case can be put up for memory being stored in the form of specially synthesized protein or nucleic acid molecules, carrying in their structure the information which makes up the memory. Or a good case can be made for memory being some kind of persistent circuit, or set of connexions, between the nerve cells. But we really do not know. And here the complications are truly enormous. The human brain, or even the brain of quite a simple organism, is something very complicated indeed, and the experimental difficulties of studying it are formidable.

Another problem we would all like to solve is that of cancer. This is the most intractable, perhaps, of all human diseases. We know enough to realize that it is caused by some kind of very fundamental derangement of the normal mechanism controlling the rate of growth and division of cells. It is a disease for which, clearly, there is not going to be any simple panacea, any pill you can take to put things right. We shall have to understand the normal working of the cell in a much more fundamental way than we do now, in order to see what happens when that goes wrong, and what to do to put it right.

As a final example of a problem to which we would particularly like to find the answer, there is the origin of life on this planet. How did life begin? The geologists and astronomers tell us about conditions on the primitive cooling earth, the sort of chemicals which were in the early atmosphere and in some kind of primeval soup or slime, or however you like to describe it, on the surface of the earth—all exposed to the radiations beating down from the sun. Not so long after the earth had cooled we find the first appearance of life and with it, presumably, this miraculous object, the self-replicating molecule of DNA. It seems such a big jump from the simple molecules which were there before, and nobody has any real idea how it happened, though there have been speculations in plenty.

Even though the rate of scientific progress is greater than ever before in the history of man, I think it may take years to discover the answers to all these questions. In all of them we are up against the problem of complexity. The models shown in the plates in this book probably seemed, when you first saw them, to illustrate very complex objects. I hope they seem rather less so now. And by comparison with the real complexities of life they are indeed rather simple. The fact is that we are very much at the beginning of the understanding of living things. And when our successors do understand some of the problems I have just mentioned, I doubt whether they will be calling themselves molecular biologists. I would guess that the author of a book like this one, writing in twenty years' time, will probably refer to molecular biology as a revolution, as I did in Chapter 1, but he will think of it simply as one of a series of revolutions, and not by then the last one.

What will the next revolution be? I cannot say. Scientists cannot predict the future any better than anyone else—even about their own field of research—but meanwhile what I can say is that, for us in this field, our present revolution is enormously exciting, and there is plenty of life in it still for a number of years to come.

Index

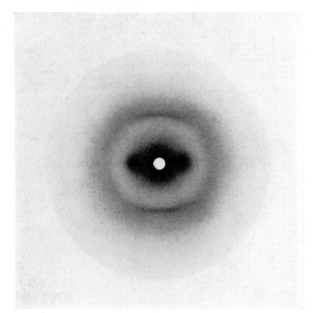

1. An early X-ray photograph of a human hair,
taken by W. T. Astbury in the 1930s.   The pattern
of dark spots and arcs shows that the keratin molecules
in the hair must be arranged in an orderly manner.
Astbury, W. T., and Bell, F. O., Cold. Spr. Hbr. Symp.
6, *109 (1938)*

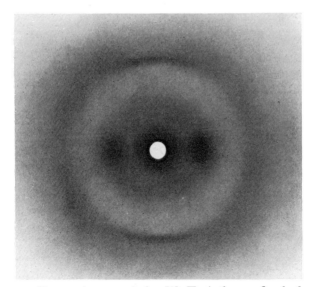

2. X-ray photograph by W. T. Astbury of a lock
of Mozart's hair, taken in 1958. *In the Novello-
Cowden Collection (Brotherton Collection), University of
Leeds*

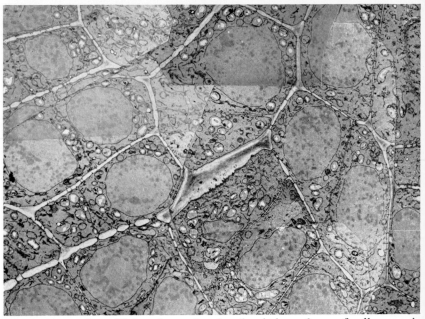

3. A thin section of living tissue, showing that it is made up of cells; magnification × 1500. This is actually a section through the growing tip of a maize root, but all other plant and animal tissues are similarly composed of aggregates of cells. *By courtesy of Dr. B. E. Juniper*

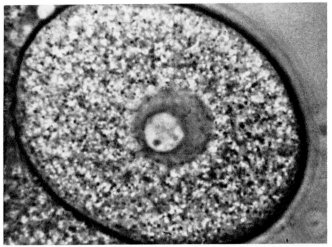

4. A single living cell. The object in the centre is the nucleus; it is surrounded by the cytoplasm and the whole is contained in the cell membrane. The cell contains many other specialized organs, not visible in this picture. A still from the film 'Development of the Nematode Worm'. *By courtesy of Eric Lucey, B.Sc., A.R.P.S., Research Film Unit, Dept. of Animal Genetics, Edinburgh University*

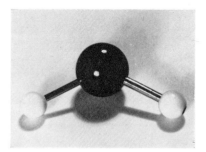

5. Space-filling model of a water molecule. The oxygen atom is coloured dark and the two hydrogens are light.

6. Ball-and-spoke model of a water molecule; oxygen atom dark, hydrogen atoms light.

7. Ball-and-spoke model of methane. The central carbon atom is connected by valency bonds to four hydrogens symmetrically arranged around it.

8. Models of the paraffin nonane, C_9H_{20}; (a) ball-and-spoke, (b) space-filling.

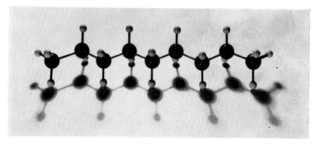

8a

8b

9. Chain of poppet beads representing a long chain polymer, (a) unfolded, (b) folded up. There are very many possible ways of folding up such a chain.

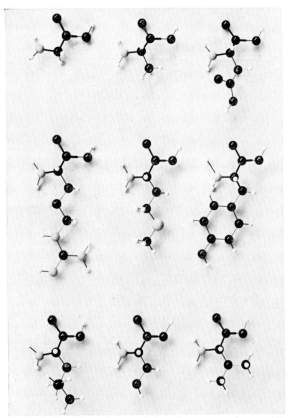

10. Ball-and-spoke models of some amino acids (the chemical formula of the same amino acids are drawn in Figure 4). The models are arranged so that the side chain, different in each amino acid, projects downwards.

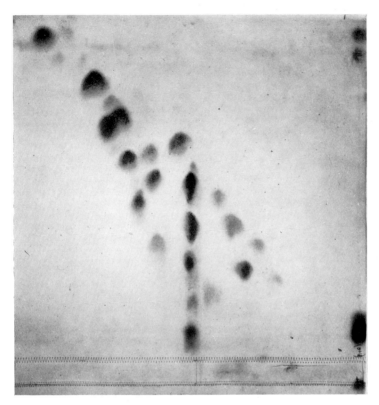

11. A typical modern chromatogram, of the kind used for separating mixtures of amino acids and peptides; they are revealed as dark spots which can be cut out of the paper and identified. *By courtesy of Dr. J. I. Harris*

12. A single crystal of common salt (sodium chloride). *By permission of the Trustees of the British Museum (Natural History)*

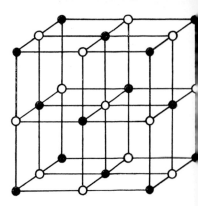

13. The arrangement of atoms a crystal of sodium chloride. Bla circles represent chlorine, emp circles sodium—or *vice versa*, for t structure is perfectly symmetric The arrangement repeats itself i definitely; each sodium has s chlorines as its nearest neighbou and *vice versa. By courtesy of Sir Lawre Bragg.* (The Crystalline State 1, 3

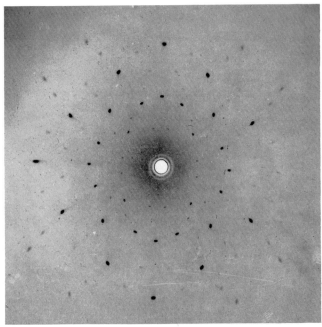

14. X-ray photograph of a crystal of sodium chloride. *By permission of the Trustees of the British Museum (Natural History)*

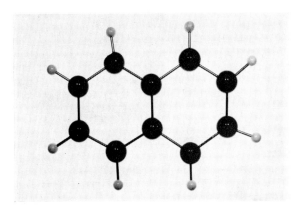

15*a*. Ball-and-spoke model of naphthalene. The black balls are carbon atoms, and the white balls are hydrogens.

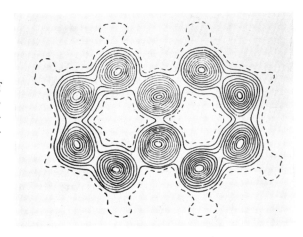

15*b*. Contour map of a naphthalene molecule, derived from X-ray analysis of a naphthalene crystal.

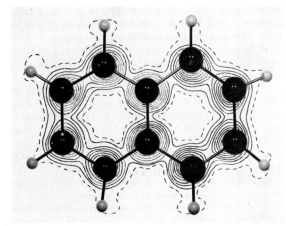

15*c*. Model and map are superimposed, showing how the contours correspond with the positions of the atoms.

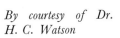

By courtesy of Dr. H. C. Watson

16.   Crystals of the protein myoglobin.   *Photograph by Dr. R. G. Parrish*

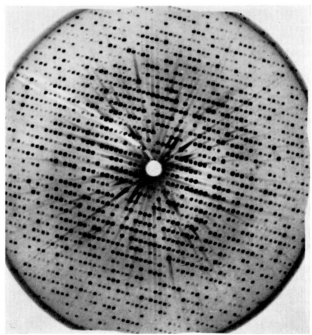

17.   X-ray photograph of a crystal of the protein myoglobin.   *Photograph by Dr. J. C. Kendrew*

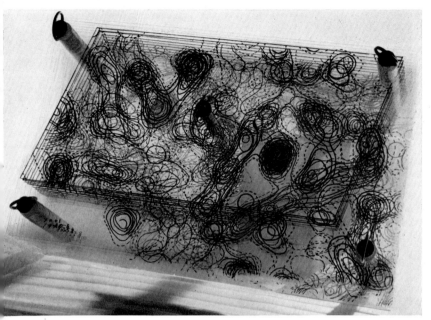

18. Three-dimensional contour map of myoglobin at low resolution. The map consists of a set of parallel transparent plastic sheets on each of which density contours are drawn; the sheets are stacked up to give a solid model. The very dense peak, right centre, is the iron atom of the haem group; embracing it, so to speak, are two segments of polypeptide chain arranged like the letter *V*.

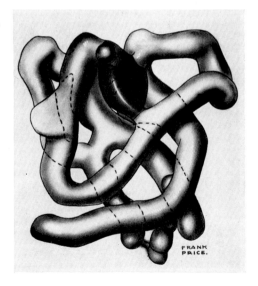

19. Low resolution model of the myoglobin molecule. The haem group is the black disk, top centre. The polypeptide chain is shown as an irregular rod winding its way round the molecule; one end of it can be seen, bottom left. The *V*-shaped segments near the haem group are the same as those visible in Plate 18.

Plates 18 and 19:
Bodo, G., Dintzis, H. M., Kendrew, J. C., and Wyckoff, H. W. Proc. Roy. Soc. A. 253, 70 *(1959)*

FRANK
PRICE.

20.   Three-dimensional contour map of myoglobin at high resolution. The dark circle, right centre, is an end-on view of a straight segment of polypeptide chain which is thus seen to be hollow —in fact a length of alpha helix.

Plates 20 and 21:
Kendrew, J. C. Les Prix Nobel en 1962, p. 103 (1963). Stockholm: Imprimerie Royale. Also Science, 139, 1259 (1963)

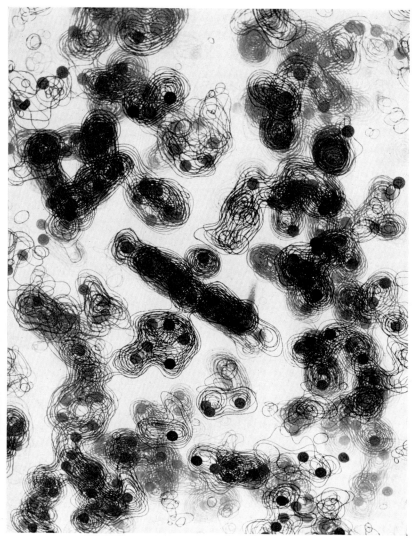

21. A close-up view of part of the high resolution contour map of myoglobin; the actual locations of atoms are shown by black disks. The flat haem group is visible edge-on (centre); also a length of helix in side view (along the bottom of picture), and another length end-on with a hole down its centre (top right).

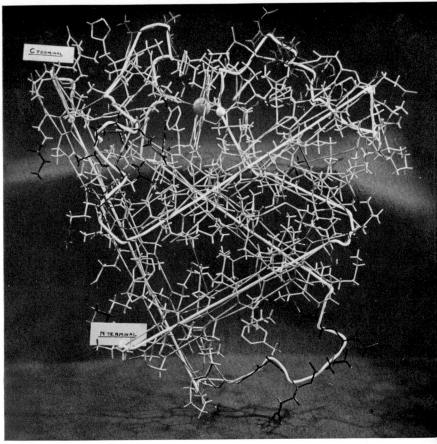

22.   Model of the myoglobin molecule showing the location of every atom.   The course of the polypeptide chain is marked with a white cord; its two ends are marked 'N-terminal and 'C-terminal'. The grey sphere is the iron atom, and the small white sphere near it shows the position of a water molecule which would be replaced by oxygen when myoglobin is oxygenated.   *Kendrew, J. C., Watson, H. C., Strandberg, B. E., Dickerson, R. E., Phillips, D. C., and Shore, V. C.* Nature, 190, *666 (1961)*

23. Space-filling model of myoglobin. *By courtesy of Dr. H. C. Watson*

24. Low resolution model of haemoglobin. The alpha chains are white and the beta chains black; two of the four haem groups are visible as grey disks. *By courtesy of Dr. M. F. Perutz*

Plates 24 and 25:
Cullis, A. F., Muirhead, H., Perutz, M. F., Rossmann, M. G., and North, A. C. T. Proc. Roy. Soc. A, 265, *161 (1962)*

25a. Taking the haemoglobin molecule to pieces—the two alpha chains are on the left and the beta chains are on the right.

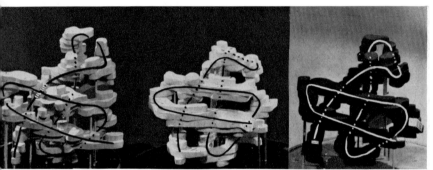

b. A comparison between the molecule of myoglobin (left) and the haemo-globin alpha chain (centre) and beta chain (right). When the three kinds of chain are arranged in the same orientation it becomes obvious that they are astonishingly similar. *By courtesy of Dr. M. F. Perutz*

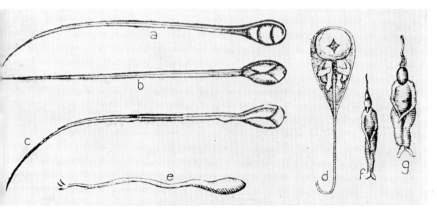

A seventeenth-century view of heredity. These are enlarged drawings of spermatozoa, in which biologists of that period believed they could see homunculi, minute replicas of human beings. *From* A History of Biology *by Charles Singer, courtesy of Messrs. Abelard-Schuman*

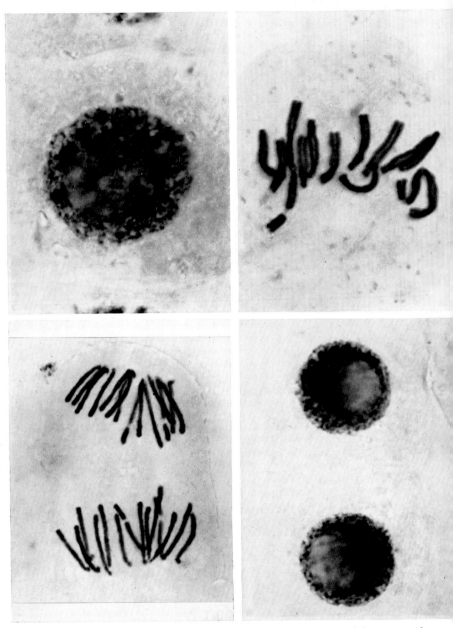

27.   Stages in the division of a cell.   (a) The nucleus of the parental cell, (b) the nucleus has broken up into separate chromosomes, each of which is double stranded, (c) the two strands of each chromosome have separated and migrated to opposite ends of the cell, (d) the two daughter nuclei.   *By courtesy of Dr. S. H. Revell*

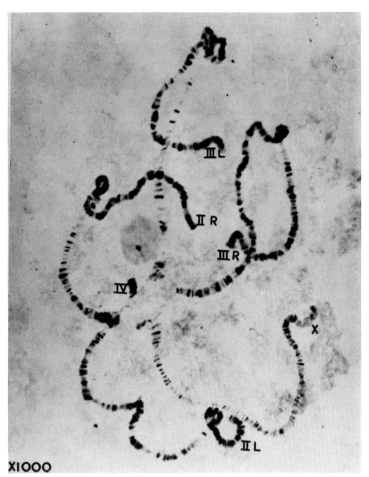

XIOOO

28. Greatly enlarged photograph of the chromosomes of *Drosophila melanogaster*, showing the band pattern. *By courtesy of Dr. B. Fahmy*

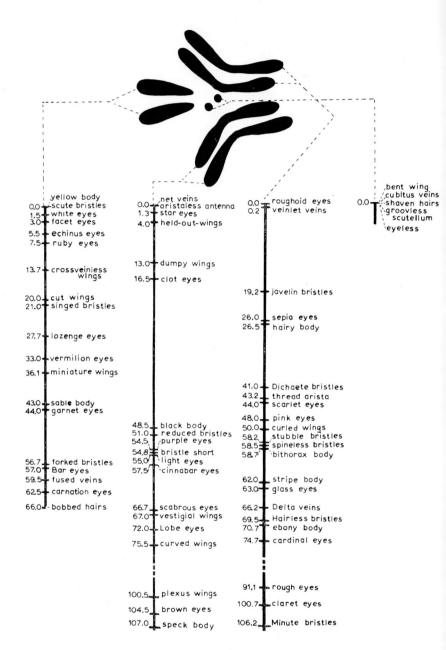

29. The chromosome map of *Drosophila melanogaster*, showing the location along each chromosome of the genes determining visible characteristics of the animal. *Redrawn from* Principles of Genetics *by Sinnott, Dunn and Dobzhansky. Copyright © McGraw-Hill, 1958. By permission of McGraw-Hill Book Company*

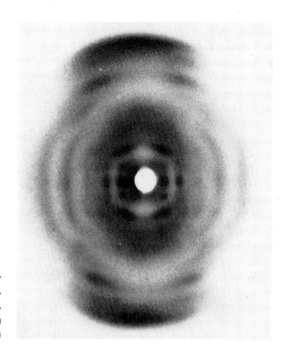

30. An early X-ray photograph of DNA, taken by W. T. Astbury in the 1930s. *Astbury, W. T.*, Symposia Soc. Exp. Biol. 1, *66 (1947)*

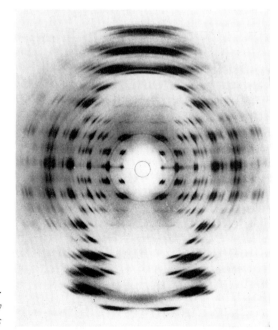

31. A modern X-ray photograph of DNA. *By courtesy of Professor M. H. F. Wilkins*

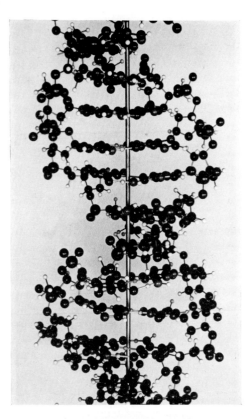

32. A model of part of the structure of DNA. The molecule must be imagined to extend a very great distance above and below the picture; it consists of two chains wound round one another and joined by pairs of bases.

33 (*below*). The thread of life—part of a single molecule of DNA photographed in the electron microscope. (The resolution is not good enough to reveal the two twisted strands of the chain.) *By courtesy of Dr. C. D. Curling*

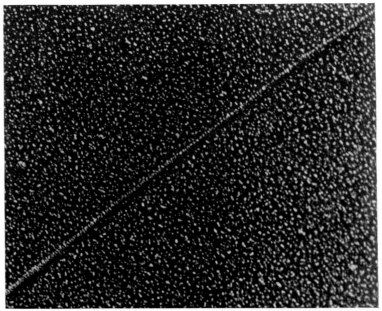

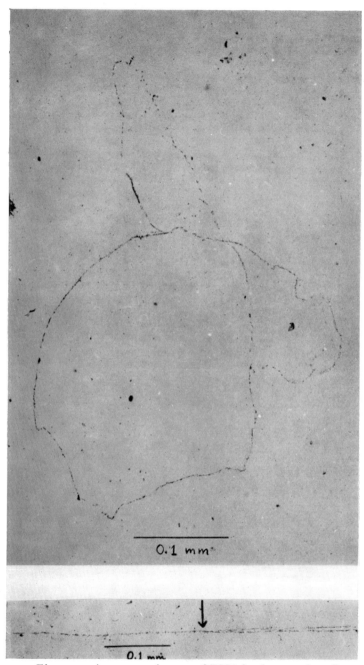

0.1 mm

0.1 mm

34. Electron microscope pictures of DNA in the act of replicating. Above, a circular DNA molecule from the bacterium
Escherichia coli; below, a DNA strand replicating at the point
indicated by the arrow. *By courtesy of Dr. F. Cairns. Upper
picture:* Cold Spr. Harb. Symp. 28, *43 (1963). Lower picture:*
J. Mol. Biol. 6, *208 (1963)*

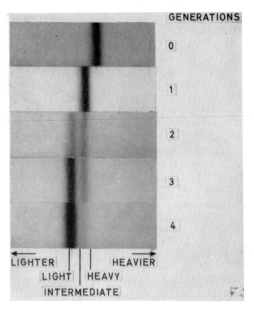

GENERATIONS

0

1

2

3

4

LIGHTER ← → HEAVIER

LIGHT | HEAVY

INTERMEDIATE

35. The Meselson-Stahl experiment. Photographs of the ultracentrifuge cell showing DNA as a dark band. The more dense the DNA, the farther to the right is the band. Above—DNA from bacteria grown in medium containing heavy nitrogen; centre—after one generation of growth in medium containing light nitrogen; below—after two generations of growth in the same medium *By courtesy of Dr. M. Meselson, unpublished*

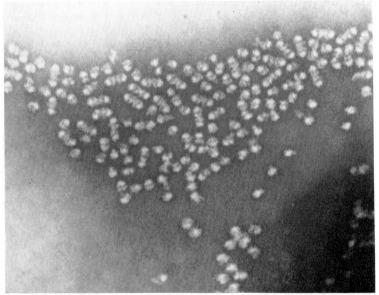

36. Ribosomes photographed under high magnification in the electron microscope. *By courtesy of Dr. H. E. Huxley*
Huxley, H. E., and Zubay, J., Mol. Biol. 2, 10 (1960)

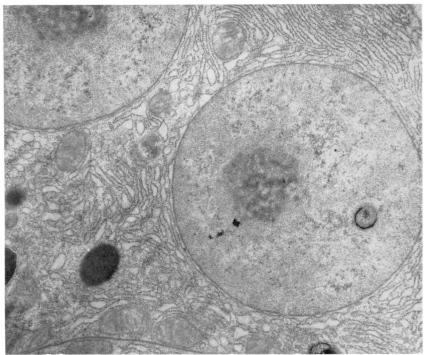

37*a*. Cell nuclei and, between them, a dense network of membranes.   The tiny black dots attached to the membranes are ribosomes.

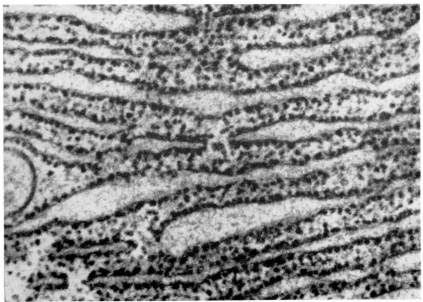

37*b*. A more highly enlarged picture of membranes with ribosomes attached.   *Both photographs by courtesy of Dr. H. E. Huxley*

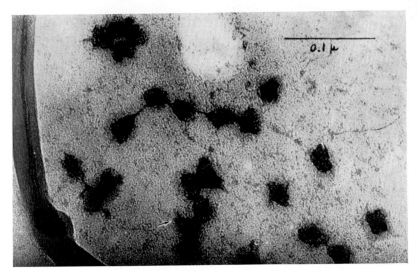

38. A greatly enlarged picture of polysomes. Ribosomes are strung along a dark thread, which is a single molecule of messenger RNA. *By courtesy of Professor A. Rich*

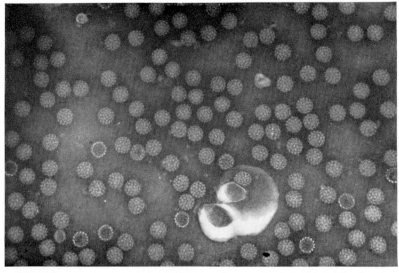

39. Electron microscope picture of a typical 'spherical' virus. This particular virus is responsible for the development of warts in human beings. *By courtesy of Dr. J. T. Finch*
Klug, A., and Finch, J. T. J. Mol. Biol., 11, 403 (1965)

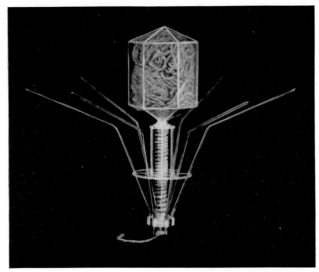

a. A model.

40*a*. and *b*. A bacteriophage before becoming attached to its host cell. *By courtesy of Dr. R. W. Horne*

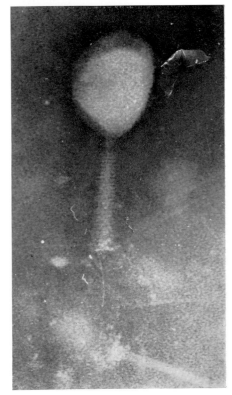

b. Electron microscope photograph.

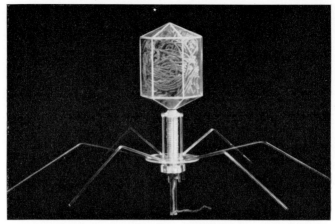

40c.   A model.

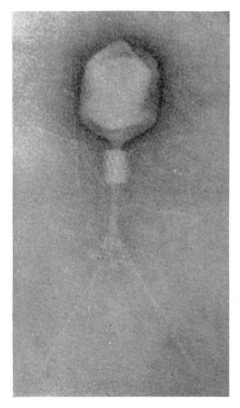

40c. and d.   A bacterio-phage after becoming attached to its host cell. *By courtesy of Dr. R. W. Horne*

40d.   Electron micro-scope photograph.

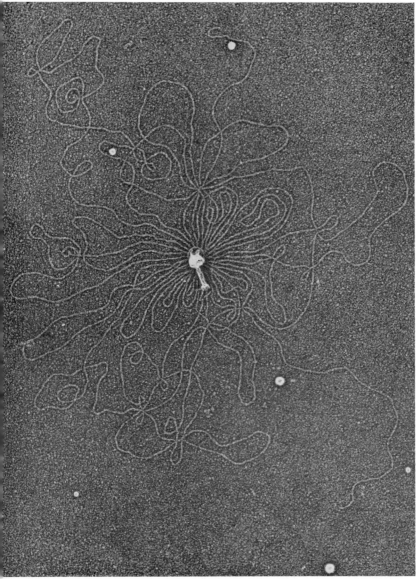

41. A bacteriophage which has burst open so that its nucleic acid has emerged as an immensely long single molecule. *By courtesy of Professor A. K. Kleinschmidt.* Biochim. et biophys. Acta, 61, *857 (1962)*

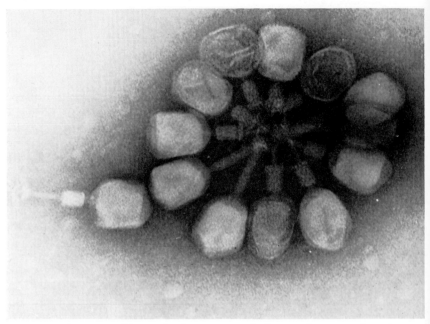

42. A group of bacteriophages, some before and some after the tail spring has been released. *By courtesy of Dr. R. W. Horne*

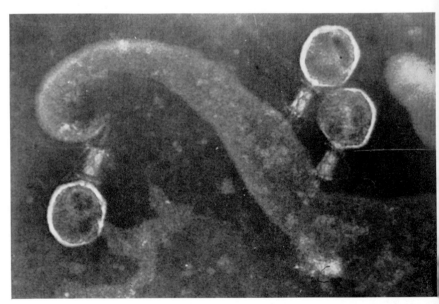

43. Bacteriophages attached to a bacterial membrane; the tail springs have been released and the 'hypodermic needle' projects through the membrane. *By courtesy of Dr. R. W. Horne*

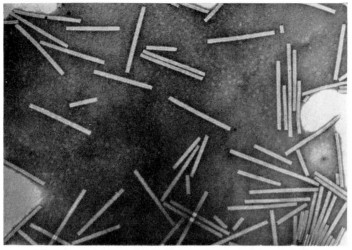

44. Electron microscope picture of particles of tobacco mosaic virus, showing the hole running along the axis. *By courtesy of Dr. J. T. Finch*

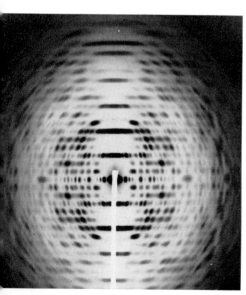

X-ray photograph of tobacco mosaic ...us. *By courtesy of Dr. K. C. Holmes*

46. A model of part of a tobacco mosaic virus particle. A few of the protein sub-units have been removed to show the helical strand of RNA. A model of the complete particle would be much longer, containing over 2,000 protein sub-units. *By courtesy of Dr. A. Klug*

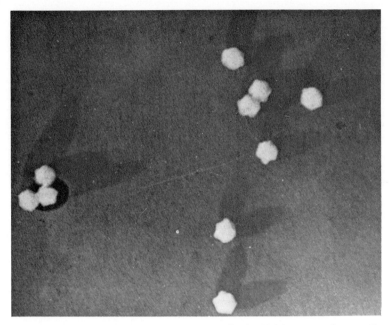

47. Double-shadowed particles of *Tipula* Iridescent virus. *By courtesy of Dr. R. C. Williams*

48. A double-shadowed particle of *Tipula* Iridescent virus and, for compariso a double-shadowed model of an icosahedron. The shadows have similar outlin showing that the virus must be icosahedral. *By courtesy of Dr. R. C. Williams* *Smith, K. M., and Williams, R. C.* Endeavour, 17, *12 (1958)*

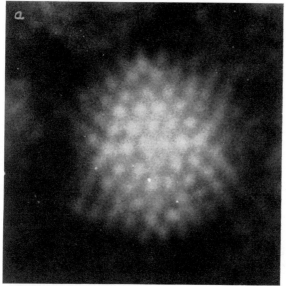

49. A single particle of adenovirus, showing triangular faces made up of sub-units, six along each edge.

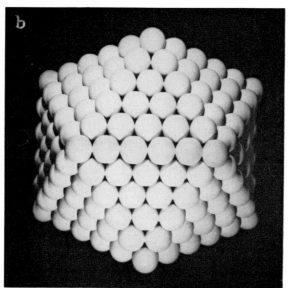

50. A model of adenovirus, constructed from 252 ping-pong balls. *Both 49 and 50 are by courtesy of Dr. R. W. Horne*
Horne, R. W., Brenner, S., Waterson, A. P., and Wildy, P., J. Mol. Biol. 1, *84* (*1959*)

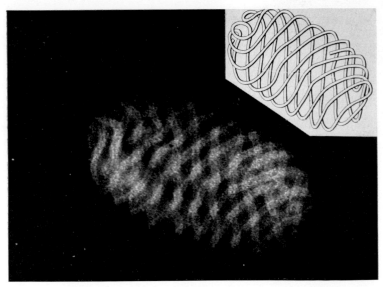

51. A particle of Orf virus, with a drawing of a model for comparison. *By courtesy of Dr. R. W. Horne*

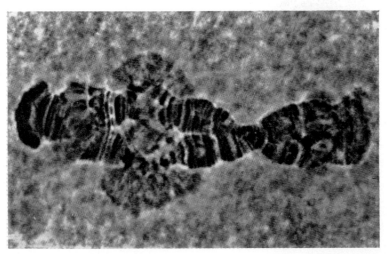

52. A photomicrograph of a single chromosome showing the band pattern and puffs where a section of the chromosome is actively engaged in producing messenger RNA. *From* Cytology *by Morison and Wilson, Reinhold Publishing Corporation*